K¹² Math⁺

About K12 Inc.

K12 Inc., a technology-based education company, is the nation's leading provider of proprietary curriculum and online education programs to students in grades K–12. K^{12} provides its curriculum and academic services to online schools, traditional classrooms, blended school programs, and directly to families. K12 Inc. also operates the K^{12} International Academy, an accredited, diploma-granting online private school serving students worldwide. K^{12}'s mission is to provide any child the curriculum and tools to maximize success in life, regardless of geographic, financial, or demographic circumstances. K12 Inc. is accredited by CITA. More information can be found at www.K12.com.

ISBN: 978-1-60153-087-5

Printed by LSC Communications/Digital, Kendallville, IN, USA, April 2017

Contents

Whole Numbers and Powers

Geometry

Fractions: Multiplication and Division

Problems Involving Fractions

Decimals: Addition and Subtraction

Decimals: Multiplication and Division

Integers

Percents and Probability

Algebra

Math Reasoning: Methods and Strategies

Math Reasoning: Solutions

Data Analysis and Representation

Round Whole Numbers in Story Problems

Round Numbers in Story Problems

Reagan wants to buy a new van. The chart shows how much a new van costs at different car dealers. Use the two strategies in the table to round each price.

	Car dealer	Friendly numbers	Nearest thousand
1.	Car Dealer A $39,528	?	?
2.	Car Dealer B $36,102	?	?
3.	Car Dealer C $38,999	?	?

4. Reagan wants to be sure he has enough money to buy the van from Car Dealer A. Which rounded number should Reagan use to estimate the amount of money he needs? Explain.

Round the numbers as directed.

5. In 1987, professional football player Walter Payton set a new record for career rushing yards. His record was 16,726 rushing yards. Round Payton's record to the nearest hundred yards.

6. The Empire State Building in New York City cost $24,718,000 to build in 1931. Round the total cost to the nearest million.

7. In 2005 there were 3,844,829 people living in Los Angeles. Round the population to the nearest ten thousand.

8. The total cost of building the Washington Monument was $1,187,710. Round the total cost to the nearest ten thousand dollars.

9. The total number of people attending professional football games for the 2007 regular season was 17,341,012. Round the total attendance to the nearest hundred thousand.

TRY IT

Choose the answer.

10. Last month the earth was about 91,348,000 miles from the sun. Which answer choice shows this distance rounded to the nearest ten million?

   A. 90,000,000 mi

   B. 91,000,000 mi

   C. 91,300,000 mi

   D. 91,400,000 mi

11. The distance between Sydney, Australia, and Paris, France, is 16,968 kilometers. Which answer choice shows this distance rounded to the nearest thousand?

   A. 14,000 km

   B. 15,000 km

   C. 16,000 km

   D. 17,000 km

12. The number of Americans who use text messaging is estimated to be more than 83,780,000. Which answer choice shows this number rounded to the nearest million?

   A. 80,000,000

   B. 83,000,000

   C. 84,000,000

   D. 90,000,000

13. The newspaper reported that the attendance at Yankee Stadium II in New York City in 2005 was 4,100,000 when rounded to the nearest hundred thousand people. Which could have been the exact attendance in 2005?

   A. 4,017,598

   B. 4,045,962

   C. 4,090,696

   D. 4,152,067

14. The height of Mount Chimborazo in Ecuador is 21,000 feet above sea level when rounded to the nearest thousand. But the height is 20,600 feet when rounded to the nearest hundred. Which could be the exact height of Mount Chimborazo?

   A. 20,458 ft

   B. 20,561 ft

   C. 20,672 ft

   D. 21,432 ft

TRY IT

Estimate and Find Sums and Differences

Estimate and Solve

Use clustering to estimate the sum. Choose the answer.

1. $377 + 386 + 372 + 389 = ?$

   A. 400

   B. 1,000

   C. 1,600

2. $43 + 32 + 44 + 35 = ?$

   A. 160

   B. 120

   C. 200

Round to friendly numbers that are multiples of 100 to estimate. Choose the answer.

3. $9,629 + 8,573 = ?$

   A. 17,000

   B. 18,200

   C. 19,200

4. $76,999 - 68,205 = ?$

   A. 6,000

   B. 7,200

   C. 8,800

Estimate by rounding the numbers to the nearest ten thousand. Choose the answer.

5. $56,880 + 43,375 = ?$

   A. 90,000

   B. 100,000

   C. 110,000

6. $325,686 - 124,478 = ?$

   A. 200,000

   B. 210,000

   C. 250,000

Complete the table. Estimate each sum or difference by using one of the strategies above. Then find the exact answer. Decide if the estimate is reasonable.

	Problem	Estimate	Exact answer
7.	$2,134 + 7,322 = ?$	?	?
8.	$34,672 - 13,440 = ?$	?	?

Estimate by first rounding the numbers to the nearest hundred thousand. Then find the exact answer. Are your estimate and exact answer close?

9. $8,925,181 + 2,820,084$

10. $8,189,378 - 5,428,310$

T R Y   I T

Estimate Sums and Differences (A)

Estimate Story Problems

Read the problem and follow the directions.

1. The Mississippi National River and Recreation Area provides food and shelter to about 50 species of mammals, 270 species of birds, 150 species of fish, and 25 species of mussels. About how many species are helped in all? Round each addend by using a friendly number that is a multiple of 25. Show your work.

2. For Problem 1, find the exact answer. Show your work.

3. In 2007, the national parks had 3,003,270 overnight visitors in tents and 5,110,811 overnight visitors in recreational vehicles. Round the addends to the nearest million. Estimate about how many overnight visitors in tents and overnight visitors in recreational vehicles there were altogether. Show your work.

4. For Problem 3, find the exact answer. Show your work.

For Problems 5–8, use a rounding strategy to round the addends. Estimate the sum and then solve the story problem.

5. The Kelly family bought a car and a van. They paid $23,956 for the car and $28,412 for the van. How much did the family spend on the two vehicles? Was your estimate close to your exact answer?

6. A website had more than 41,252,000 visitors in 2005. In 2006, there were 12,452,000 visitors. What was the total number of visitors for the two years? Was your estimate close to your exact answer?

7. In 2007, Los Angeles had a population of 3,834,340 and San Diego had a population of 1,266,731. What was the total population of Los Angeles and San Diego? Was your estimate close to your exact answer?

8. In the election for city mayor, the winner received 76,262 votes, and the other person running received 73,672 votes. How many total votes were cast? Was your estimate close to your exact answer?

Choose the answer.

9. A large bin held 56,360 marbles. A small bin held 17,580 marbles. Find the exact answer. How many marbles were in both bins?

   A. 38,780   B. 63,940   C. 73,940   D. 74,940

TRY IT

Estimate Sums and Differences (B)

Practice Estimating with Subtraction

Solve. Show your work.

1. British astronomer William Herschel discovered the planet Uranus in 1781. In the year 2015, how long will it have been, rounded to the nearest hundred, since Uranus was discovered?

2. For Problem 1, find the exact difference.

3. Satellite orbits vary in their distance from the earth. Orbits can be anywhere from 252,800 to 35,200,000 yards. What is the greatest distance between satellite orbits? Round to the nearest ten thousand to estimate.

4. For Problem 3, find the exact difference.

Use a rounding strategy to round the numbers. Estimate the difference. Then find the exact answer. Explain whether your estimate was reasonable.

5. Last year the local newspaper printed 931,244 newspapers. This year it printed only 310,201 newspapers. How many fewer newspapers did it print this year?

6. Sofia's mom traveled 78,109 miles for work two years ago. Last year she traveled 21,311 miles. How many more miles did she travel two years ago than last year?

Choose the answer.

7. During last year's baseball season, 52,462 people attended the local team's home games. This year, only 33,200 people attended the home games. If you round each number to the nearest ten thousand, what is the estimated difference between the attendance in the two years?

   A. 9,000   B. 19,000   C. 20,000   D. 21,000

8. When the Smiths bought their house, they paid $480,400. Several years later, the price rose to $590,500. How much more is the house worth now than when they bought it? Find the exact answer.

   A. $111,000   B. $110,100   C. $101,100   D. $100,110

TRY IT

Estimate and Find Products and Quotients

Estimate and Calculate Products and Quotients

Choose the answer that gives the closest estimate.

1. Find the upper bound estimate for
   $834 \times 24 = ?$

   A. 30

   B. 21,300

   C. 27,000

2. Find the lower bound estimate for
   $305 \times 439 = ?$

   A. 120,000

   B. 280,000

   C. 420,000

3. Round to the greatest place value to
   estimate $5,781,493 \div 789 = ?$

   A. 6,250

   B. 7,500

   C. 8,000

4. Use a friendly number for the dividend to
   estimate $30,138,275 \div 6 = ?$

   A. 3,800,000

   B. 5,000,000

   C. 10,600,000

Complete the table. Estimate each product or quotient by using one of
the strategies above. Then find the exact answer. Show any remainder as a
fraction. Decide if the estimate is reasonable.

	Problem	Estimate	Exact answer
5.	$19 \times 212 = ?$	?	?
6.	$81,291 \div 9 = ?$	?	?
7.	$389 \times 28 = ?$	?	?

Estimate to find the correct answer.

8. Estimate the product.

   $98 \times 586 = \underline{\ ?\ }$

9. Estimate the quotient.

   $68,488 \div 34 = \underline{\ ?\ }$

10. Estimate and then solve.

    $5,011 \times 97 = \underline{\ ?\ }$

    For Problem 10, was your estimate
    close to your exact answer?

11. Estimate and then solve.

    $55,138 \div 11 = \underline{\ ?\ }$

    For Problem 11, was your estimate
    close to your exact answer?

TRY IT

Estimate Products and Quotients (A)

Estimate and Find Products

Read the problem and follow the directions.

1. Five years ago, 312 pumpkins were grown on Harvest Farm. This year, 22 times that many were grown. Estimate by rounding the first factor to the greater ten and the second factor to the lesser ten. About how many pumpkins were grown on Harvest Farm this year? Choose the answer.

   A. 250   B. 6,400   C. 10,000   D. 12

2. For Problem 1, find the exact answer.

3. For Problem 1, explain why your estimate was reasonable.

4. There are 112 delivery trucks for Wholesome Snacks Factory. Each truck averages 342 miles of deliveries each week. Estimate by rounding the first factor to the lesser hundred and the second factor to the greater hundred. About how many total miles are driven in one week of deliveries? Choose the answer.

   A. 45,000,000   B. 200   C. 40,000   D. 3,000

5. For Problem 4, find the exact answer.

6. For Problem 4, explain why your estimate was reasonable.

7. Estimate by rounding the number of vehicles to the nearest million and then multiplying. There were 7,667,066 passenger vehicles sold in the United States in one year. If the same number of vehicles were sold each year for the next 8 years, about how many vehicles would be sold?

8. Estimate by rounding each number to the nearest ten. A highway in Alaska is 545 miles long. If 28 cars drove the entire length of the highway, about how many miles would they have driven in all?

T R Y   I T

9. Estimate by rounding the distance to the nearest thousand miles and multiplying. Then find the exact answer. Nara travels 9 round trips between Atlanta and Dubai every year. Each round trip is a total of 24,386 mi. How far does she travel in one year?

10. For Problem 9, was your estimate close to your exact answer?

11. Estimate by rounding the number of wing flaps to the nearest ten and multiplying. Then find the exact answer. A hummingbird flapped its wings 63 times in one second. How many times would the hummingbird flap its wings in 120 seconds?

12. For Problem 11, was your estimate close to your exact answer?

Choose the answer.

13. The elephants at the zoo eat about 1,416 pounds of grass every day. Rounding the amount of grass to the nearest hundred pounds, about how many pounds of grass would the elephants eat in 7 days?

A. 200   B. 2,000   C. 9,800   D. 98,000

14. Kelly's scout troop handed out flyers for a fundraiser. There were 40 girls and they each handed out 134 flyers. How many flyers did they hand out in all?

A. 40

B. 134

C. 536

D. 5,360

Estimate Products and Quotients (B)

Estimate and Calculate Quotients

Worked Examples

You can estimate and calculate the solution to a division story problem.

PROBLEM The Intercity Bus Line takes passengers from Atlanta, Georgia, to Seattle, Washington. The trip lasts 4 days and the distance is 2,692 miles. If the bus travels the same number of miles each day, how many miles a day will it travel?

SOLUTION

Trip from Atlanta, Georgia, to Seattle, Washington			
	Total distance (miles)	Number of days	Miles each day
First estimate			
Second estimate			
Exact answer			

Read the problem. Make a table. Find the information in the problem that tells you the distance between Atlanta and Seattle and how many days the trip lasts.

1 **First estimate:** Round the total distance in miles to the nearest hundred. Record the number of days of the trip. Divide the rounded total distance by the number of days. Record the quotient, which is an estimate of the miles traveled each day.

2 **Second estimate:** Round the total distance in miles to the nearest thousand. Record the number of days of the trip. Divide the rounded total distance by the number of days. Record the quotient, which is another estimate of the miles traveled each day.

3 **Exact answer:** Record the total distance in miles. Record the number of days of the trip. Divide the total distance by the number of days. Record the quotient, which is the exact number of miles the bus will travel each day.

4 Write the estimates and the exact answer below the table, and compare them. The estimate of 675 miles each day is close to the exact answer, 673 miles. It is a reasonable estimate. The estimate of 750 miles each day is not close to the exact answer, 673 miles.

L E A R N

ANSWER

Trip from Atlanta, Georgia, to Seattle, Washington			
	Total distance (miles)	Number of days	Miles each day
First estimate	2,700	4	675
Second estimate	3,000	4	750
Exact answer	2,692	4	673

First estimate: 675 miles
Second estimate: 750 miles
Exact answer: 673 miles

The bus will travel 673 miles each day.

LOOK BACK To solve the problem, you estimated before you calculated the exact answer. You used two different estimation strategies to round the numbers in the problem. One estimate was closer to the exact answer. Some estimates are more reasonable in a problem than others.

Read the problem and follow the directions.

Every summer, the Intercity Bus Line carries eager vacationers 767 miles from Bloomington, Indiana, to Ocean City, Maryland. The passengers would like the trip to take 13 hours. How many miles does the bus need to travel each hour to make the trip in 13 hours?

1. Fill out the table as you answer the following questions. Use the table in the Worked Examples box as a model.

Trip from Bloomington, Indiana, to Ocean City, Maryland			
	Total distance (miles)	Number of hours	Miles each hour
First estimate			
Second estimate			
Exact answer			

LEARN

2. For the first estimate, round the distance to the nearest hundred.

   What is the distance to the nearest hundred?

3. Round the number of hours to the nearest ten.

   What is the number of hours rounded to the nearest ten?

4. Divide. For the first estimate, how many miles each hour will the bus need to travel?

5. For the second estimate, round the distance to the lesser hundred.

   What is the distance rounded to the lesser hundred?

6. Round the number of hours to the lesser ten.

   What is the number of hours rounded to the lesser ten?

7. Divide. For the second estimate, how many miles each hour will the bus need to travel?

8. For the exact answer, write the total distance and number of hours from the problem. Divide the total distance by the number of hours. What is the exact number of miles the bus will need to travel each hour?

   Check to see that you have filled in all the cells in the table.

9. Write *first estimate*, *second estimate*, and *exact answer* below the table. Write the estimates and exact answers, including the label "miles," next to the descriptions.

Estimate Products and Quotients (B)

Understand Story Problem Remainders

Worked Examples

When you answer whole-number division story problems, the quotient may have a remainder. To solve the problem, you need to decide what to do with the remainder in a way that makes sense for that story problem.

There are three strategies for solving division problems that have a remainder:

1 Write the quotient as a fraction or a mixed number.

2 Write the quotient as a whole number and a remainder. Increase the quotient by 1 and drop the remainder.

3 Write the quotient as a whole number and a remainder. Keep the quotient and ignore the remainder.

In this division story problem, the meaning of the remainder tells you which strategy to use.

PROBLEM Winnie calls Serena 4 times in one day. They talk for a total of 15 minutes. Each phone call lasts exactly the same amount of time. If the phone company charges Winnie for every minute of a call, even if only part of a minute is included in the call, how many minutes will the company charge Winnie for each of her 4 calls?

SOLUTION
Use each strategy to solve the problem.

STRATEGY 1
- Show the answer as a mixed number. $15 \div 4 = 3\frac{3}{4}$
- Each of Winnie's calls lasts $3\frac{3}{4}$ minutes.

STRATEGY 2
- Increase the quotient by 1 and drop the remainder.
- Each of Winnie's calls is shown as 4 minutes, rather than $3\frac{3}{4}$ minutes, if this strategy is used.

STRATEGY 3
- Keep the quotient and ignore the remainder.
- Each of Winnie's calls is shown as 3 minutes, rather than $3\frac{3}{4}$ minutes, if this strategy is used.

LEARN

ANSWER Strategy 2 is the answer. Since Winnie is charged for every minute of a phone call, even if it's only a part of a minute, the answer to the problem is that each call is 4 minutes. You increase the quotient by 1 and drop the remainder.

Strategy 1 isn't the answer. If you write the quotient as a mixed number, then each call lasted $3\frac{3}{4}$ minutes. But the problem says that Winnie is charged for each minute, even if it's only a part of a minute. The answer $3\frac{3}{4}$ minutes doesn't solve the problem.

Strategy 3 isn't the answer. If you keep the quotient and ignore the remainder, then each call is 3 minutes. You know that each call lasted $3\frac{3}{4}$ minutes and that Winnie is charged for each minute, including a part of a minute. The answer of 3 minutes doesn't solve the problem.

Read the problem and follow the directions.

Intercity Bus Line pays its drivers for every whole mile they drive in a day. A driver drove a total of 9,901 miles, driving the same number of miles each day for 25 days. For how many miles each day did the company pay him?

1. What is the answer you need to find?

2. What part of the problem tells you how to decide what to do with the remainder?

3. Write a number sentence showing the quotient as a mixed number.

4. Can you solve the problem by writing the quotient as a mixed number? Why?

5. Can you solve the problem by writing the quotient as a whole number and remainder, and then increase the quotient by 1 and drop the remainder? Why?

6. Can you solve the problem by writing the quotient as a whole number and a remainder, and then keep the quotient and ignore the remainder? Why?

LEARN

A driver for Intercity Bus Line drove 707 miles last week. If she drove for 14 hours, driving the same distance every hour, how many miles did she drive each hour?

7. Write the question you are being asked.

8. Explain how the question helps you decide what to do with the remainder.

9. Write a number sentence showing the quotient as a whole number and a remainder.

10. Solve the problem by using the strategies to decide what to do with the remainder. Explain your answer.

LEARN

Estimate Products and Quotients (B)

Story Problems About Division Estimates

Read the problem and follow the directions.

1. The combined number of miles driven in one day by 78 of Intercity Bus Line's drivers was 23,790 miles. Each driver drove the same number of miles. Estimate how many miles each driver drove in one day by rounding the number of miles to the greater thousand and the number of buses to the greater ten. Choose the answer.

   A. 15

   B. 100

   C. 300

   D. 3,000

2. For Problem 1, find the exact answer.

3. For Problem 1, explain why your estimate was reasonable.

4. A delivery driver has a short route. He has traveled this route for 1,065 miles, and he has driven it 24 times. Estimate the route's number of miles by rounding the driver's total miles driven to the lesser thousand and the number of trips he drove to the lesser ten. Choose the answer.

   A. 50

   B. 70

   C. 300

   D. 7,000

5. For Problem 4, find the exact answer.

6. For Problem 4, explain what to do with the fraction part of the mixed number in the exact answer and why.

7. The brick company made 892,322 bricks in 12 months, and they made the same number of bricks each month. Estimate about how many bricks the company made in 1 month by rounding the number of bricks to the nearest hundred thousand.

TRY IT

Choose the answer.

8. Estimate by rounding the number to the nearest thousand. Jimmy drove 13,981 miles in 2007. This was about two times as far as he drove in 2005. About how many miles did Jimmy drive in 2005?

A. 690

B. 6,900

C. 7,000

D. 70,000

TRY IT

Bases and Exponents (A)

Evaluate Expressions

Read the problem and follow the directions.

1. Write 36^2 using repeated multiplication.

2. Draw a sketch to show 6^2.

3. Find the value of 36^2.

4. Write 5^3 using repeated multiplication.

5. Write $27 \times 27 \times 27$ as a single base with an exponent.

6. Write $77 \cdot 77$ as a single base with an exponent.

7. Write 8^3 using repeated multiplication, and then compute the value.

8. Write 7^2 using repeated multiplication, and then compute the value.

Write the base and exponent for the expression.

9.

Exponent form	14^2
Base	?
Exponent	?

10.

Exponent form	20^3
Base	?
Exponent	?

Choose the answer.

11. What is another way to write 43^3?

   A. $3 \cdot 43$ B. $43 \cdot 43 \cdot 43$ C. $3 \cdot 4 \cdot 3$ D. $3 \cdot 3 \cdot 3$

12. Which expression shows $24 \cdot 24$ written as a base and an exponent?

   A. 224   B. $24 \cdot 2$ C. 24^2 D. $2 \cdot 24$

13. Which expression shows 68^2 by using repeated multiplication?

   A. $68 \cdot 2$ B. $2 \cdot 2$ C. $6 \cdot 8 \cdot 2$ D. $68 \cdot 68$

TRY IT

14. Which model shows 7^2?

A.

B.

C.

D.

15. Which model shows 4^3?

A.

B.

C.

D.

TRY IT

Bases and Exponents (B)

Work with Exponents of 4 and 5

Read the problem and follow the directions.

1. Write 5^4 using multiple factors.

2. Write 17^5 using multiple factors.

3. Write 8^4 using multiple factors, and then compute the value.

4. Write 4^5 using multiple factors, and then compute the value.

5. Write $33 \cdot 33 \cdot 33 \cdot 33$ as a single base with an exponent.

Write the base and exponent for the expression.

6.

Exponent form	23^5
Base	?
Exponent	?

7.

Exponent form	18^5
Base	?
Exponent	?

Choose the answer.

8. What is another way to write 26^4?

   A. $26 \cdot 26 \cdot 26 \cdot 26$

   B. $26 \cdot 4$

   C. $2 \cdot 6 \cdot 4$

   D. $26 \cdot 26 \cdot 26 \cdot 26 \cdot 26$

9. Which shows a true statement?

   A. $5^4 > 4^5$

   B. $5^4 < 4^5$

   C. $5^4 = 4^5$

   D. $5^4 + 4^5 = 54$

10. Which shows $12 \cdot 12 \cdot 12 \cdot 12 \cdot 12$ written as a single base with an exponent?

    A. 5^{12}

    B. 12^{12}

    C. 12^5

11. Compare 13^4 and $13 \cdot 13 \cdot 13$. Which statement is true?

    A. $13^4 < 13 \cdot 13 \cdot 13$

    B. $13^4 = 13 \cdot 13 \cdot 13$

    C. $13^4 > 13 \cdot 13 \cdot 13$

12. Compare 4^3 and 3^4. Which statement is true?

    A. $4^3 < 3^4$

    B. $4^3 = 3^4$

    C. $4^3 > 3^4$

T R Y   I T

Solve Problems Involving Powers

Solve Problems with Exponents

For Problems 1–6, complete the table. Use each of the Answer Options to find the equal factors and the standard form for each expression.

Base and Exponent Table				Answer Options	
Expression	Equal factors	Standard form		Equal factors	Standard form
1. 3^4	?	?		A. $5 \cdot 5$	G. 4,096
2. 2^4	?	?		B. $6 \cdot 6 \cdot 6$	H. 512
3. 8^3	?	?		C. $3 \cdot 3 \cdot 3 \cdot 3$	I. 25
4. 5^2	?	?		D. $8 \cdot 8 \cdot 8$	J. 81
5. 8^4	?	?		E. $2 \cdot 2 \cdot 2 \cdot 2$	K. 216
6. 6^3	?	?		F. $8 \cdot 8 \cdot 8 \cdot 8$	L. 16

Compare. Write $<$, $>$, or $=$.

7. $8^2 \square 2^5$

8. $6^3 \square 8^2$

9. $2^4 \square 3^3$

10. $3^4 \square 9^2$

Read the problem and follow the directions.

11. What number is the greatest square of a whole number that evenly divides 54?

12. What number is the greatest cube of a whole number that evenly divides 54?

13. Tina called 5 people on Monday. Those 5 people each called 5 different people on Tuesday. On Wednesday, the people who were called on Tuesday each called 5 different people.

   Write an expression with an exponent to solve the problem.

   How many calls were made on Wednesday?

TRY IT

14. Write the whole number that makes a true statement.

$9^2 = \square^4$

15. Jeff e-mailed 4 people on Sunday. On Monday, each of those 4 people e-mailed 4 different people. On Tuesday, each person who was e-mailed on Monday e-mailed 4 different people.

Write an expression with an exponent to solve the problem.

How many people were e-mailed on Tuesday?

Choose the answer.

16. Compare 3^4 and 4^3.
Which statement is true?

A. $3^4 > 4^3$

B. $3^4 = 4^3$

C. $3^4 < 4^3$

17. Compare 6^2 and 4^4.
Which statement is true?

A. $6^2 = 4^4$

B. $6^2 < 4^4$

C. $6^2 > 4^4$

TRY IT

Prime Factorization

Find Prime Factorization

Make a factor tree for the composite number. Then show the composite number as the product of prime factors. Use powers of prime factors when possible.

1. 42

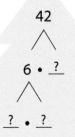

2. 20

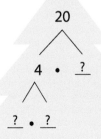

3. 27

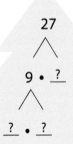

4. 48

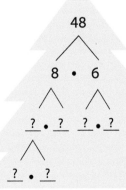

Read the problem and follow the directions.

5. Write the prime factorization of 24.

6. Write the prime factorization of 18 using powers of prime numbers.

7. Write 3 whole numbers less than 50 that have prime factors of only 2 or 3.

TRY IT

8. Allen said the prime factorization of 45 is 5 • 9. Is he correct?
   If he is wrong, explain why he is wrong, and write the correct answer.

9. Tom made this factor tree for 90. Make a different factor tree for 90.
   Write the prime factorization for both trees.

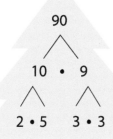

Choose the answer.

10. Which of the following shows the prime
    factorization of 30?

    A. 2 • 3 • 5

    B. 5 • 6

    C. 1 • 2 • 2 • 5

    D. 3 • 10

11. Which of the following shows 28 factored
    into powers of prime numbers?

    A. 3^2 • 7

    B. 2 • 2 • 7

    C. 2^2 • 7

    D. 4 • 7

TRY IT

Angles (A)
Measure Angles

Use a protractor to measure the angle. Write the angle measure.

1.

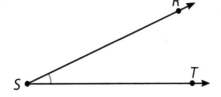

2.

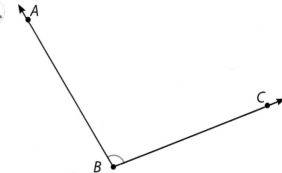

3.

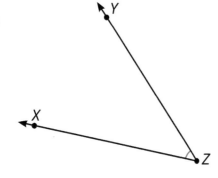

4.

5.

T R Y   I T

6.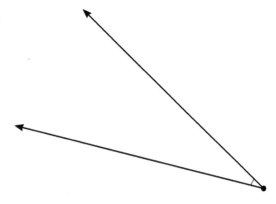

7.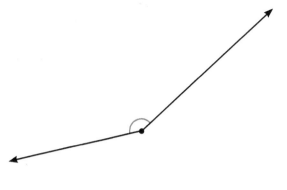

Draw the given angle.

8. obtuse angle

9. acute angle

10. straight angle.

11. 90° angle
Name the angle as either an acute angle, an obtuse angle, a right angle, or a straight angle.

Choose the answer.

12. Classify this angle.

A. acute

B. obtuse

C. right

D. straight

13. Classify this angle.

A. acute

B. obtuse

C. right

D. straight

14. Which is an obtuse angle?

A.

B.

C.

D.

TRY IT

Use a protractor to measure the angle. Record the measures and describe
the angle as acute, right, obtuse, or straight.

1.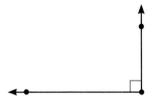

2.

3.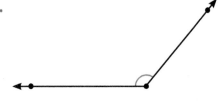

4.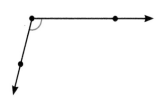

Use a ruler and a protractor to draw the angle to the given measure.
Describe the angle as acute, right, obtuse, or straight.

5. 110°

6. 35°

7. 90°

8. Draw a straight angle, label the center B, and show the angle measure.

9. Draw a 45° angle.

10. Draw a 120° angle.

11. Draw a 160° angle.

12. Draw a 180° angle.

TRY IT

Perpendicular and Parallel Lines

Practice Types of Lines

Answer the question and draw lines as directed.

1. What are perpendicular lines?

2. Give one example of perpendicular lines that you see around you every day.

3. Construct perpendicular lines using a compass and ruler.

4. What are intersecting lines?

5. Give one example of intersecting lines that you see around you every day.

6. Draw intersecting lines.

7. What are parallel lines?

8. Give one example of parallel lines that you see around you every day.

9. Construct parallel lines, using a compass and a ruler.

Choose the answer.

10. Identify these lines.

    A. parallel

    B. perpendicular

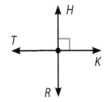

11. Identify lines *EF* and *GH*.

    A. parallel

    B. perpendicular

T R Y   I T

Construct Triangles and Quadrilaterals

Construct Each Shape

Worked Examples

You can construct and draw perpendicular lines.

PROBLEM Draw a line perpendicular to line segment *AB*.

SOLUTION

1 Draw a line segment about 3 inches long. Label the endpoints *A* and *B*.

2 Set the point of the compass at point *A*. Open the compass a width that is not all the way to point *B*, but beyond the middle of the line segment. Draw an arc that extends from above the middle of the line segment to below the middle of the line segment.

3 Leave the compass the same width and set the point of the compass at point *B*. Draw a second arc that crosses the first arc both above and below the line segment. Label the point where the arcs cross above the line segment as point *C* and the point where the arcs cross below the line segment as point *D*.

4 Use a ruler to draw line *CD*, which will be perpendicular to line segment *AB*. Label the point where line *CD* and line segment *AB* intersect as point *E*.

5 Use a protractor to measure angles *CEA* and *CEB*. Check that each angle measures exactly 90°. Angles *DEA* and *DEB* will also measure exactly 90°.

ANSWER

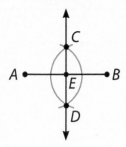

L E A R N

Follow the step-by-step directions to construct the shape.

1. equilateral triangle

STEP **1** Draw line segment *JK*.

STEP **2** Place the point of the compass on point *J* and the pencil at point *K*. Draw an arc with the center at point *J* and radius *JK* that extends above the line segment.

STEP **3** Without changing the size of the compass opening, draw an arc with center at point *K* that intersects the first arc.

STEP **4** Label the point where the arcs intersect point *L*.

STEP **5** Draw line segments that connect point *L* to point *J* and point *L* to point *K*. Triangle *JLK* is equilateral.

2. square

STEP **1** Draw line segment *OP*.

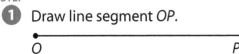

STEP **2** Place the point of the compass on point *O* and the pencil at point *P*. Draw an arc with the center at point *O* and radius *OP* that extends above and below the line segment.

STEP **3** Without changing the size of the compass opening, draw an arc with center at point *P* that intersects the first arc at two points. Label one point *Q* and one point *R*.

STEP **4** Draw the line segment that connects points *Q* and *R*. Label the line segment *n* and the intersection of this line segment with line segment *OP* as point *S*.

STEP **5** Draw a circle with center at point *S* and radius *SP*.

STEP **6** The circle will intersect with line segment *n* at two points. Label these points *T* and *U*.

STEP **7** Draw line segments *OT*, *TP*, *PU*, and *UO*. The resulting figure is a square.

3. right triangle

STEP **1** Draw a line segment and mark point *A* on the line segment.

STEP **2** Place the point of the compass on point *A*. Draw an arc on the right end of the line segment from point *A*. Label the intersection point *B*.

L E A R N

3 Leave the compass the same width and place the point of the compass on point *A*. Draw a second arc on the left end of the line segment from point *A* and label this point *C*.

4 Open the compass a little more and set the point of the compass on point *B*. Draw an arc over point *A* above the line segment.

5 Leave the compass the same width and set the point of the compass on point *C*. Draw an arc over point *A* above the line segment.

6 Mark the point where the arcs meet point *D*.

7 Use a ruler to draw perpendicular line segment *AD*.

8 Use a ruler to draw line segment *DB*. Triangle *DAB* is a right triangle.

4. rectangle

1 Draw line segment *AB*.

```
•————————————————————•
A                    B
```

2 Place the point of the compass on point *A* and the pencil at point *B*. Draw an arc with the center at point *A* and radius *AB* that extends above and below the line segment.

3 Leave the compass the same width and draw an arc with center at point *B* that intersects the first arc at two points. Label these two points of intersection *C* and *D*.

4 Draw the line segment that connects points *C* and *D*. Label the line segment *e* and the intersection of this line segment with line segment *AB* as point *F*.

5 Draw a circle with center at point *F* and radius *FB*.

6 The circle will intersect with line segment *e* at two points. Label these points *G* and *H*.

7 Draw line segments *AG*, *GB*, *BH*, and *HA*. The resulting figure is a square.

8 Use a ruler to extend line segment *AG*. Mark point *I* at the end of line segment *AG*.

9 Use a ruler to extend line segment *HB*. Make sure to extend line segment *HB* so that it is the same length as line segment *AI*. Mark point *J*.

10 Use a ruler to connect points *I* and *J*. The resulting figure is a rectangle.

LEARN

Construct Triangles and Quadrilaterals

Practice Triangles and Quadrilaterals

Draw the shape.

1. square

2. rectangle

3. equilateral triangle

4. right triangle

Use a compass and ruler to construct the shape.

5. right triangle

6. rectangle

T R Y   I T

Angles and Triangles (A)

Measure Angles in Triangles

Worked Examples

You can use a protractor to measure angles in a triangle.

PROBLEM Review how to use a protractor to measure angle *FGH*.

SOLUTION

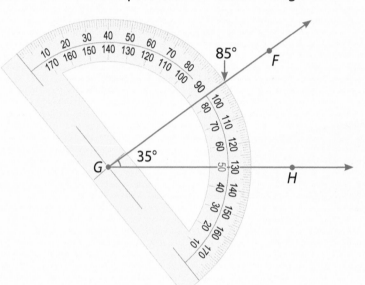

1. Place the center of the protractor on the vertex of the angle. Have one of the angle's rays pass through a friendly degree measure on the inner scale. A friendly degree measure is a number on the protractor's scale that makes it easy for you to use mental math to add and subtract.

2. Use 50° as a friendly degree measure. You could choose a different friendly degree measure, but you should always get the same results.

3. Note where the other angle's ray is passing through the protractor. Subtract the lesser measure on the protractor's scale, 50°, from the greater measure, 85°, to find the angle's measure.

4. $85 - 50 = 35$

ANSWER Angle *FGH* measures 35°.

Use these steps to measure the triangle's three angles. Then add the angle measures. The sum of the angle measures should be 180°.

LEARN

Use a protractor to measure the angles in the triangle. Then find the sum of the angle measures. Classify the triangle as acute, right, obtuse, or equiangular.

1.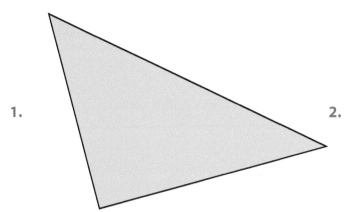

2.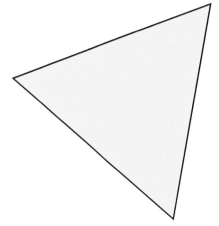

3.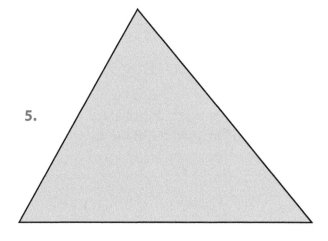

4.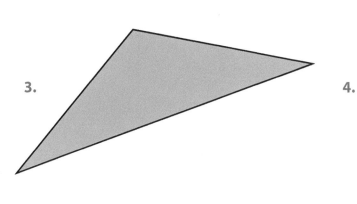

5.

6.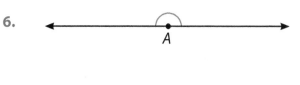

A

L E A R N

Angles and Triangles (B)

Find Missing Angle Measures

The sum of the angle measures of any triangle is 180°. Find the missing angle measure in the triangle.

1.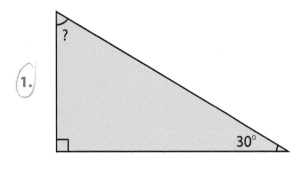
   ?
   30°

2. ?
   35°   130°

3.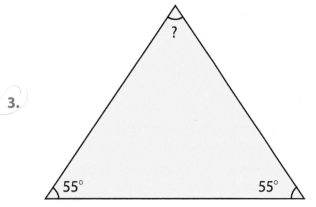
   ?
   55°   55°

4. 92°
   28°
   ?

5.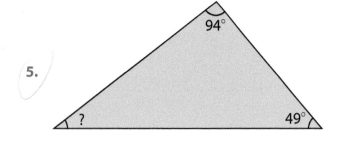
   94°
   ?   49°

TRY IT

Read the problem and follow the directions.

6. Claire was asked to draw a triangle with 3 angles measuring 15°, 15°, and 160°. Will she be able to draw a triangle with these angle measures?

   Explain your answer.

7. Alyssa was asked to draw a triangle with 3 angles measuring 42°, 68°, and 70°. Will she be able to draw a triangle with these angle measures?

   Explain your answer.

8. Jaime was asked to draw a triangle with 3 angles measuring 77°, 23°, and 79°. Will he be able to draw a triangle with these angle measures?

   Explain your answer.

9. Jacob made a triangular pennant for a football game. One angle measure is 40°. Another angle measure is 70°. What is the measure of the third angle?

10. The sign over the entrance to a tree house is the shape of a triangle. The measures of the angles of the triangle are equal. What is the measure of each angle?

11. One angle of a right triangle is 40°. What is the measure of each of the other two angles?

12. Angles K and M of triangle KLM each measure 35°. What is the measure of angle L?

Choose the answer.

13. What is the measure of ∠Y?

    A. 8°

    B. 12°

    C. 88°

    D. 92°

14. What is the measure of ∠L?

    A. 53°

    B. 89°

    C. 91°

    D. 119°

    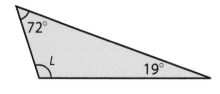

15. What is the measure of ∠R?

    A. 41°

    B. 49°

    C. 82°

    D. 98°

TRY IT

Angles in a Quadrilateral (A)

Measure Angles

Worked Examples

You can use a protractor to measure angles in a quadrilateral.

PROBLEM Review how to use a protractor to measure angle *FGH*.

SOLUTION

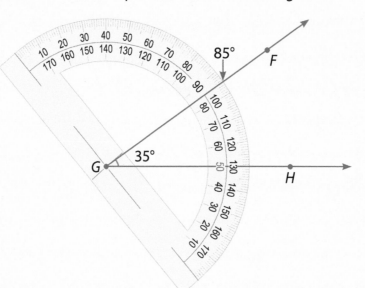

1. Place the center of the protractor on the vertex of the angle. Have one of the angle's rays pass through a friendly degree measure on the inner scale. A friendly degree measure is a number on the protractor's scale that makes it easy for you to use mental math to add and subtract.

2. Use 50° as a friendly degree measure. You could choose a different friendly degree measure, but you should always get the same results.

3. Note where the other angle's ray is passing through the protractor. Subtract the lesser measure on the protractor's scale, 50°, from the greater measure, 85°, to find the angle's measure.

4. $85 - 50 = 35$

ANSWER Angle *FGH* measures 35°.
Use these steps to measure the quadrilateral's four angles. Then add the angle measures. The sum of the angle measures should be 360°.

Use a protractor to measure the angles in the quadrilateral. Then find the sum
of the angle measures and write the name of the quadrilateral.

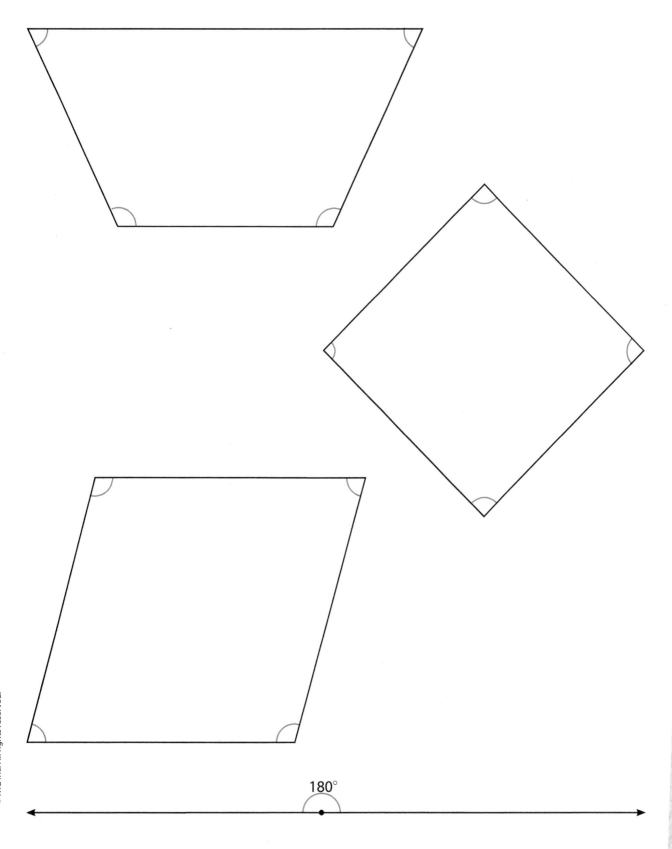

180°

LEARN

Measure each angle on the quadrilateral. Use a protractor or angle ruler.
Then find the sum of the angle measures.

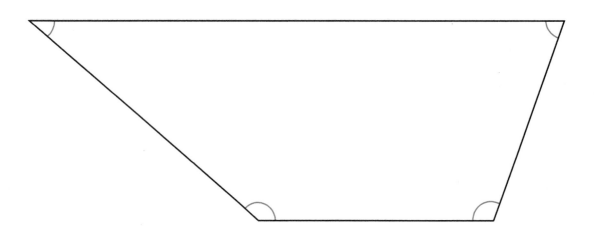

180°

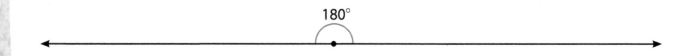

38

LEARN

Angles in a Quadrilateral (B)

Practice Quadrilateral Angles

Solve.

1. A quadrilateral has angles that measure 77°, 108°, and 65° What is the measure of the fourth angle?

2. A quadrilateral has angles that measure 91°, 96°, and 88°. What is the measure of the fourth angle?

3. A quadrilateral has angles that measure 87°, 69°, and 104° What is the measure of the fourth angle?

4. What is the measure of angle K?

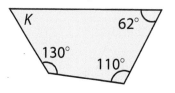

5. What is the measure of ∠B?

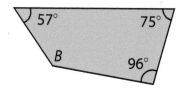

6. What is the measure of ∠S?

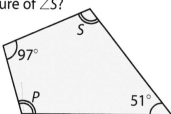

7. What is the measure of ∠E?

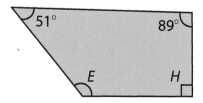

Choose the answer.

8. What is the measure of ∠C?

   A. 83°   B. 93°

   C. 103°   D. 123°

9. What is the measure of ∠C?

   A. 68°   B. 78°

   C. 88°   D. 98°

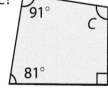

10. What is the measure of ∠F?

    A. 97°   B. 101°

    C. 111°   D. 121°

TRY IT

Transformations (B)

Tessellations Practice

Read the problem and follow the directions.

1. What is a transformation?

2. Think about a tessellation you have made or one you have seen in a picture. Describe the transformations that are used to make the tessellation.

Sketch the answer.

3. Show a counterclockwise rotation of this shape.

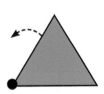

4. Show a reflection of this shape over the dotted line.

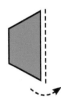

5. Show a translation of this shape.

6. Draw a counterclockwise rotation around the dot of this picture of a crayon.

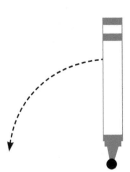

TRY IT

7. Draw a reflection of this picture of a hairbrush over the dotted line.

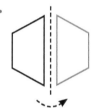

8. Draw a translation of this picture of a toothbrush diagonally in the direction of the dotted line.

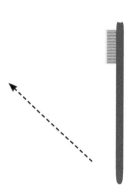

Choose the answer that describes the transformation.

9.

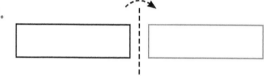

A. The shape has been moved sideways.

B. The shape has been flipped over the line.

C. The shape has been turned around a point.

10.

A. The shape has been reflected.

B. The shape has been rotated.

C. The shape has been translated.

11.

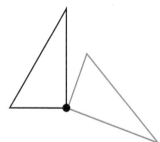

A. reflection

B. rotation

C. translation

12.

A. rotation

B. translation

C. reflection

TRY IT

Draw 2-D Views of 3-D Objects

Draw and Sketch Views

Draw the top, front, and side view of the object.

1.

2.

3.

4.

5.

6.

Draw the view as directed.

7. Draw the top view of this object.

8. Draw the side view of this object.

9. Draw the top view of this object.

10. Draw the side view of this object.

Choose the answer.

11. Which shows the view of the base of this object?

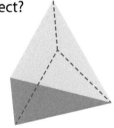

A.   B.

C.   D.

12. Six solids are joined together to make this object. Which shows the top view of this object?

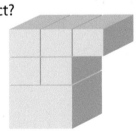

A.    B.

C.   D.

TRY IT

Unit Review

Checkpoint Practice

Solve.

1. Which is an obtuse angle?

A.  15°

B.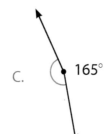

C. 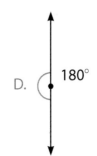 165°

D. 180°

Use a protractor to find the measure of the angle.

2.

    A. 50°
    B. 120°
    C. 130°
    D. 150°

3.

    A. 20°
    B. 30°
    C. 150°
    D. 160°

4.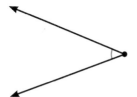

    A. 42°
    B. 52°
    C. 132°
    D. 142°

5.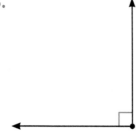

    A. 70°
    B. 80°
    C. 90°
    D. 180°

UNIT REVIEW

Choose the answer.

6. Look at the blue lines in each picture. Which pair is an example of parallel lines?

A.  B. 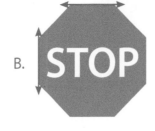 C.  D.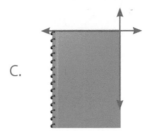

7. Which is an example of perpendicular lines?

A. 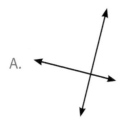 B. 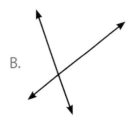 C. 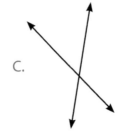 D.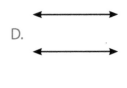

8. Identify these lines.

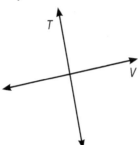

A. parallel   B. perpendicular

9. Look at the blue line segments in the picture. Identify the line segments.

A. perpendicular   B. parallel

10. A triangle has angles that measure 57° and 44°. What is the measure of the third angle?

A. 13°

B. 79°

C. 99°

D. 101°

11. A triangle has angles that measure 11° and 88°. What is the measure of the third angle?

A. 12°

B. 79°

C. 81°

D. 98°

UNIT REVIEW

12. What is the measure of ∠M?

A. 42°

B. 90°

C. 138°

D. 180°

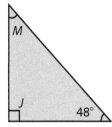

13. What is the measure of ∠D?

A. 25°

B. 65°

C. 115°

D. 155°

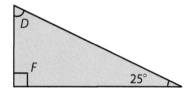

14. What is the measure of ∠R?

A. 13°

B. 52°

C. 76°

D. 104°

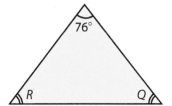

15. What is the measure of ∠F?

A. 66°

B. 76°

C. 106°

D. 116°

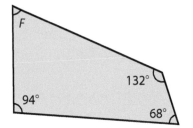

16. Which shows a reflection of the trapezoid?

A.

B.

C.

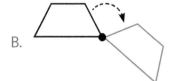

17. Which shows a rotation of the apple?

A.

B.

C.

18. Describe this transformation.

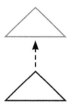

A. rotation

B. reflection

C. translation

19. Describe this transformation.

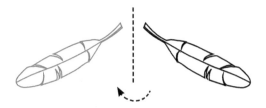

A. translation

B. rotation

C. reflection

U N I T   R E V I E W

20. Describe this transformation.

  A. reflection

  B. rotation

  C. translation

21. Describe this transformation.

  A. rotation

  B. translation

  C. reflection

22. Which shows the top view of this object?

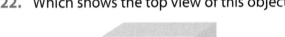

  A.   B.

  C.   D.

23. Which shows the top view of this object?

  A.   B.

  C.   D.

24. Which shows the side view of this object?

  A.   B.

  C.    D.

25. Which shows the top view of this object?

  A.    B.

  C.   D.

UNIT REVIEW

Use Models to Multiply Fractions

Multiply Fractions

Explain how to solve the problem. Then find the answer.

1. $\frac{4}{4} \times \frac{3}{5} = \underline{\ ?\ }$

2. $\frac{2}{5} \times \frac{2}{2} = \underline{\ ?\ }$

Use grid paper models to solve. Write the product in simplest form.

3. $\frac{2}{3} \times \frac{6}{6} = \underline{\ ?\ }$

4. $\frac{3}{5} \times \frac{1}{4} = \underline{\ ?\ }$

5. $\frac{3}{8} \times \frac{3}{2} = \underline{\ ?\ }$

6. $\frac{5}{5} \times \frac{9}{11} = \underline{\ ?\ }$

7. $\frac{5}{10} \times \frac{7}{7} = \underline{\ ?\ }$

Choose the answer. Use grid paper models to solve. Be sure the answer is in simplest form.

8. $\frac{3}{4} \times \frac{5}{5} = ?$

   A. $\frac{3}{4}$ B. $\frac{8}{9}$ C. $\frac{8}{20}$ D. $\frac{15}{9}$

9. $\frac{4}{4} \times \frac{1}{2} = ?$

   A. $\frac{4}{6}$ B. $\frac{5}{6}$ C. $\frac{1}{2}$ D. $\frac{5}{8}$

T R Y   I T

Understand Division of Fractions

Practice Dividing Fractions

Read the problem and follow the directions.

1. What is $\frac{9}{18}$ in simplest form?

2. What is $\frac{8}{24}$ in simplest form?

3. Explain how to solve this problem:
$$\frac{5}{7} \div \frac{6}{6} = \underline{\ ?\ }$$

Solve. Write the product in simplest form.

4. $\frac{2}{5} \div \frac{2}{2} = \underline{\ ?\ }$

5. $\frac{6}{8} \div \frac{4}{4} = \underline{\ ?\ }$

6. $\frac{8}{9} \div \frac{4}{4} = \underline{\ ?\ }$

7. $\frac{1}{2} \div \frac{3}{3} = \underline{\ ?\ }$

Choose the answer. Be sure the answer is in simplest form.

8. $\frac{2}{3} \div \frac{6}{6} = \ ?$

   A. 2   B. 3

   C. $\frac{2}{3}$ D. $\frac{3}{2}$

9. $\frac{3}{5} \div \frac{7}{7} = \ ?$

   A. 3   B. 5

   C. $\frac{3}{5}$ D. $\frac{5}{3}$

10. $\frac{1}{9} \div \frac{5}{5} = \ ?$

   A. $\frac{1}{9}$ B. 1

   C. 9   D. $\frac{9}{5}$

11. $\frac{3}{4} \div \frac{2}{2} = \ ?$

   A. 3   B. $\frac{4}{3}$

   C. $\frac{3}{4}$ D. 4

TRY IT

Multiply Fractions (A)

Practice Multiplying

Use models or an algorithm to solve. Write the product in simplest form.

1. $\frac{4}{5} \times \frac{7}{8} = \underline{\ ?\ }$

2. $\frac{3}{10} \times \frac{5}{12} = \underline{\ ?\ }$

3. $\frac{5}{8} \times \frac{4}{5} = \underline{\ ?\ }$

4. $\frac{3}{4} \times \frac{2}{9} = \underline{\ ?\ }$

Explain how to solve the problem by dividing out common factors of numerators and denominators. Then find the answer.

5. $\frac{3}{4} \cdot \frac{2}{9} = \underline{\ ?\ }$

6. $\frac{3}{5} \cdot \frac{2}{3} = \underline{\ ?\ }$

Choose the answer. Be sure the answer is in simplest form.

7. $\frac{2}{3} \times \frac{5}{7} = ?$

    A. $\frac{7}{10}$ B. $\frac{29}{21}$ C. $\frac{10}{21}$ D. $\frac{7}{21}$

8. $\frac{3}{5} \times \frac{4}{5} = ?$

    A. $\frac{12}{25}$ B. $\frac{12}{5}$ C. $\frac{3}{4}$ D. $\frac{7}{5}$

9. $\frac{1}{5} \times \frac{6}{7} = ?$

    A. $\frac{7}{12}$ B. $\frac{6}{35}$ C. $\frac{6}{7}$ D. $\frac{7}{30}$

10. $\frac{3}{4} \times \frac{3}{6} = ?$

    A. $\frac{6}{10}$ B. $\frac{6}{24}$ C. $\frac{3}{8}$ D. $\frac{9}{10}$

TRY IT

Multiply Fractions (B)

Multiply Mixed Numbers

Solve using models or an algorithm. Write the product in simplest form.

1. $\frac{5}{6} \times \frac{3}{4} = $ _?_

2. $1\frac{4}{8} \times \frac{1}{2} = $ _?_

3. $3\frac{3}{7} \times \frac{5}{8} = $ _?_

4. $\frac{2}{9} \times 2\frac{1}{2} = $ _?_

Explain how to solve the problem. Then solve the problem.

5. $\frac{1}{8} \times 2\frac{2}{3} = $ _?_

6. $\frac{4}{7} \times 2\frac{1}{6} = $ _?_

7. A baker used $2\frac{1}{3}$ packages of raisins when he was making muffins. Each package contained $\frac{3}{4}$ pound of raisins.

   How many pounds of raisins did the baker use?

Choose the answer.

8. $4\frac{3}{4} \times \frac{2}{3} = ?$

   A. $\frac{21}{7}$ B. $4\frac{6}{12}$

   C. $\frac{38}{7}$ D. $3\frac{1}{6}$

9. $2\frac{1}{4} \times \frac{3}{7} = ?$

   A. $\frac{9}{14}$ B. $\frac{12}{11}$

   C. $\frac{18}{24}$ D. $\frac{27}{28}$

10. $\frac{3}{5} \times 2\frac{5}{6} = ?$

    A. $1\frac{7}{10}$ B. $2\frac{1}{2}$

    C. $\frac{20}{30}$ D. $\frac{32}{10}$

T R Y I T

Multiply Fractions (C)

Practice Multiplying Fractions

Explain each step in solving the problem.

1. $\frac{4}{5} \cdot 10 = \underline{\ ?\ }$

2. $4\frac{2}{5} \cdot 3\frac{4}{7} = \underline{\ ?\ }$

Multiply. Express your answer in simplest form.

3. $\frac{6}{10} \cdot 30 = \underline{\ ?\ }$

4. $4\frac{1}{2} \cdot 1\frac{2}{3} = \underline{\ ?\ }$

5. $\frac{5}{8} \cdot \frac{3}{10} = \underline{\ ?\ }$

6. $2\frac{1}{10} \cdot \frac{4}{7} = \underline{\ ?\ }$

Explain each step in solving the story problem.

7. Jordan bought 12 apples. Three-fourths of them were red.

   How many red apples did Jordan buy?

8. Samantha was able to shovel $3\frac{3}{4}$ sidewalks in front of neighbors' houses in an hour.

   How many sidewalks could she shovel in $1\frac{1}{3}$ hours?

Choose the answer. Be sure the answer is in simplest form.

9. $\frac{3}{4} \cdot 5 = ?$

   A. $\frac{3}{20}$

   B. $\frac{15}{20}$

   C. $3\frac{3}{4}$

   D. $5\frac{3}{4}$

10. $3\frac{1}{4} \cdot 2\frac{2}{5} = ?$

   A. $\frac{25}{20}$

   B. $\frac{65}{48}$

   C. $6\frac{1}{10}$

   D. $7\frac{4}{5}$

T R Y   I T

Divide Fractions (A)

Practice Fraction Division

Solve. Write your answer in simplest form.

1. $6 \div \frac{3}{8} = \underline{\quad?\quad}$

2. $\frac{2}{3} \div \frac{4}{6} = \underline{\quad?\quad}$

3. $\frac{1}{5} \div \frac{6}{10} = \underline{\quad?\quad}$

4. $\frac{3}{7} \div \frac{1}{2} = \underline{\quad?\quad}$

5. $\frac{2}{5} \div \frac{7}{10} = \underline{\quad?\quad}$

Explain how to solve the problem.

6. $\frac{5}{7} \div \frac{1}{4} = \underline{\quad?\quad}$

7. $\frac{3}{4} \div \frac{1}{2} = \underline{\quad?\quad}$

8. $\frac{1}{2} \div \frac{1}{8} = \underline{\quad?\quad}$

Choose the answer.

9. Which is the first step to write to solve this problem? $\frac{5}{12} \div \frac{3}{4} = ?$

   A. $\frac{5}{12} \times \frac{4}{3} = ?$

   B. $\frac{12}{5} \times \frac{3}{4} = ?$

   C. $\frac{5}{12} \div \frac{4}{3} = ?$

   D. $\frac{12}{5} \div \frac{3}{4} = ?$

Choose the answer. Be sure the answer is in simplest form.

10. $\frac{8}{12} \div \frac{4}{7} = ?$

    A. $1\frac{1}{6}$

    B. $\frac{12}{19}$

    C. $\frac{14}{13}$

    D. $\frac{56}{16}$

TRY IT

Divide Fractions (B)

Practice Dividing Fractions

Solve using the algorithm. Write your answer in simplest form.

1. $3\frac{1}{12} \div \frac{6}{8} = \underline{?}$

2. $4 \div \frac{3}{9} = \underline{?}$

3. $5\frac{2}{3} \div \frac{7}{10} = \underline{?}$

4. $7\frac{9}{10} \div \frac{1}{2} = \underline{?}$

5. It is $2\frac{1}{4}$ miles to the pool. If you rest every $\frac{1}{4}$ mile, how many times will you rest?

Explain how to solve the problem.

6. A builder owned $8\frac{4}{5}$ acres of land. He wanted to divide it into smaller lots. He wanted each lot to be $\frac{3}{10}$ acre. How many lots could the builder make?

7. $4\frac{2}{9} \div \frac{4}{6} = \underline{?}$

Choose the answer. Be sure the answer is in simplest form.

8. $3\frac{3}{9} \div \frac{3}{5} = ?$

A. $5\frac{5}{9}$ B. 2 C. 5 D. $3\frac{5}{9}$

9. $2\frac{2}{3} \div \frac{2}{3} = ?$

A. $\frac{12}{4}$ B. $\frac{24}{3}$ C. $\frac{16}{9}$ D. 4

10. $2\frac{1}{4} \div \frac{4}{6} = ?$

A. $\frac{27}{6}$ B. $\frac{8}{24}$ C. $3\frac{3}{8}$ D. $\frac{15}{8}$

T R Y   I T

Divide Fractions (C)

Divide Mixed Numbers and Fractions

Solve using an algorithm. Write your answer in simplest form.

1. $\frac{2}{5} \div \frac{3}{7} = \underline{\ ?\ }$

2. $5 \div \frac{2}{3} = \underline{\ ?\ }$

3. $\frac{3}{12} \div \frac{1}{3} = \underline{\ ?\ }$

4. $\frac{3}{4} \div \frac{1}{2} = \underline{\ ?\ }$

5. $\frac{5}{6} \div 2 = \underline{\ ?\ }$

6. $3\frac{2}{3} \div 1\frac{2}{6} = \underline{\ ?\ }$

7. $6 \div \frac{3}{5} = \underline{\ ?\ }$

8. $\frac{4}{7} \div 10 = \underline{\ ?\ }$

9. $5\frac{2}{3} \div \frac{4}{6} = \underline{\ ?\ }$

10. $7\frac{5}{8} \div \frac{3}{4} = \underline{\ ?\ }$

TRY IT

11. A recipe uses $3\frac{5}{6}$ cups of flour. The chef measures out $1\frac{1}{3}$ cups of flour at a time. How many times will he measure $1\frac{1}{3}$ cups until he reaches $3\frac{5}{6}$?

12. The area of the room is $7\frac{1}{4}$ feet². The length is $2\frac{2}{3}$ feet.

How long is the width?

Choose the answer. Be sure the answer is in simplest form.

13. $\frac{3}{7} \div 2\frac{1}{2} = ?$

   A. $\frac{15}{14}$
   B. $\frac{5}{12}$
   C. $\frac{6}{35}$
   D. $\frac{5}{1}$

14. $\frac{2}{5} \div 4\frac{1}{3} = ?$

   A. $\frac{6}{18}$
   B. $\frac{5}{18}$
   C. $\frac{26}{15}$
   D. $\frac{6}{65}$

15. $4\frac{1}{4} \div 2\frac{1}{6} = ?$

   A. 2
   B. $1\frac{25}{26}$
   C. $\frac{30}{10}$
   D. $\frac{20}{15}$

Explain how to solve the problem. Write your answer in simplest form.

16. Rosa has a magnetic strip $9\frac{3}{4}$ inches long. She wants to cut the strip to make magnets that are each $1\frac{1}{2}$ inches long.

   How many magnets can Rosa make?

TRY IT

Solve Fraction Story Problems (A)

Understand Multiplication Story Problems

Worked Examples

You can write a number sentence to set up the solution for the following multiplication story problem:

- A cabinet that you are building will be $4\frac{1}{2}$ feet tall. The doorknob needs to be placed $\frac{5}{6}$ of the way up from the bottom of the cabinet. How high should you place the doorknob?

PROBLEM 1 Write a number sentence that you can use to solve the multiplication story problem.

SOLUTION

1. Read the problem.

2. Decide what question needs to be answered. For this problem, you need to find where you will place the doorknob.

3. Decide what operation you need to use. For this problem, you need to use multiplication to find out what $\frac{5}{6}$ of $4\frac{1}{2}$ equals.

4. Write a number sentence that finds the product of the factors $4\frac{1}{2}$ and $\frac{5}{6}$.

ANSWER $4\frac{1}{2} \times \frac{5}{6} = ?$

PROBLEM 2 Solve the number sentence you wrote for Problem 1.

SOLUTION

1. Write the number sentence that solves the problem: $4\frac{1}{2} \times \frac{5}{6} = ?$

2. Change $4\frac{1}{2}$ to an improper fraction: $\frac{9}{2} \times \frac{5}{6} = ?$

3. Divide out the common factors. 3 is a common factor of 9 and 6: $\frac{3}{2} \times \frac{5}{2} = ?$

4. Multiply the numerators, and multiply the denominators: $\frac{15}{4}$

5. Change the improper fraction to a mixed number: $\frac{15}{4} = 3\frac{3}{4}$

6. $4\frac{1}{2} \times \frac{5}{6} = 3\frac{3}{4}$

ANSWER The knob should be $3\frac{3}{4}$ feet from the bottom of the cabinet.

Write a number sentence for each problem. Then go back and solve the problems.

1. You are painting a large toy box.
   The paintbrush is $\frac{3}{10}$ feet wide.

   If it takes 9 brushstrokes to paint across the side, how long is the side?

2. You are building a kitchen table.
   You want to put glass inserts, or pieces, in the middle.

   If the table will be $2\frac{1}{4}$ yards in length and the length of the inserts will be $\frac{4}{6}$ of the table's length, how long will the inserts be?

3. You are repairing a closet door.
   The length of the door is $2\frac{6}{9}$ feet.
   A design on the door is $\frac{3}{4}$ of the door's length.

   What is the length of the design on the door?

4. A tree house you are building requires pieces of wood that are $2\frac{6}{12}$ feet wide.

   If $52\frac{1}{2}$ of those pieces of wood are laid side to side between tree limbs to create the floor, how wide is the floor?

5. A railing is around the tree house.
   A total of $5\frac{1}{4}$ pieces of wood that are $3\frac{2}{7}$ feet long are used to create the railing.

   How long is the railing?

LEARN

Solve Fraction Story Problems (A)

Practice Solving Story Problems

Write a number sentence for the problem. Then solve the problem. Express your answer in simplest form.

1. A ball was dropped from a height of 18 m.
   It bounced back $\frac{5}{6}$ of that original height on the first bounce.
   How high did the ball bounce back on the first bounce?

2. Mr. Jones bought $5\frac{1}{4}$ yards of fabric.
   He gave his son $\frac{3}{7}$ of the fabric.
   How much fabric did he give his son?

TRY IT

3. Dan is painting a mural that measures $3\frac{1}{2}$ ft by $5\frac{2}{3}$ ft.

   What is the area of the mural?

4. Fred finished his book in $2\frac{1}{3}$ hours.
   Alex took $1\frac{1}{2}$ times longer than Fred to finish.

   How long did it take Alex to finish his book?

Choose the answer. Be sure the answer is in simplest form.

5. The width of a television screen is $\frac{4}{5}$ the length. The length of the television screen is $3\frac{3}{4}$ ft. What is the width?

   A. 2 ft

   B. $2\frac{2}{5}$ ft

   C. $2\frac{3}{5}$ ft

   D. 3 ft

6. A recipe asks for $3\frac{1}{2}$ cups of milk. How much milk is needed to make $1\frac{1}{2}$ recipes?

   A. $4\frac{1}{4}$ cups

   B. $4\frac{1}{2}$ cups

   C. $5\frac{1}{4}$ cups

   D. $5\frac{1}{2}$ cups

TRY IT

Solve Fraction Story Problems (B)

Work with Fraction Story Problems

Worked Examples

You can write a number sentence to set up the solution for the following division story problem:

- The organizers of a 10K race have $9\frac{3}{5}$ boxes of medium T-shirts to give to runners. Each registration table for the race will get $2\frac{2}{5}$ boxes. How many registration tables will there be?

PROBLEM 1 Write a number sentence that you can use to solve the division story problem.

SOLUTION

1. Read the problem.

2. Decide what question needs to be answered. For this problem, you need to find how many registration tables there will be at the race.

3. Decide what operation you need to use. For this problem, you need to use division to find the quotient of $9\frac{3}{5}$ divided by $2\frac{2}{5}$.

4. Write a number sentence that finds the quotient of the dividend $9\frac{3}{5}$ and the divisor $2\frac{2}{5}$.

ANSWER $9\frac{3}{5} \div 2\frac{2}{5} = ?$

PROBLEM 2 Solve the number sentence you wrote for Problem 1.

SOLUTION

1. Write the number sentence that solves the problem: $9\frac{3}{5} \div 2\frac{2}{5} = ?$

2. Change $9\frac{3}{5}$ and $2\frac{2}{5}$ to improper fractions: $\frac{48}{5} \div \frac{12}{5} = ?$

3. Change the division problem to a multiplication problem using the reciprocal of the divisor: $\frac{48}{5} \times \frac{5}{12} = ?$

4. Divide out the common factors. 5 is a common factor of 5 and 5. 12 is a common factor of 48 and 12: $\frac{4}{1} \times \frac{1}{1} = ?$

5. Multiply the numerators, and multiply the denominators: $\frac{4}{1} = 4$

6. $9\frac{3}{5} \div 2\frac{2}{5} = 4$

ANSWER There will be 4 registration tables.

LEARN

Write a number sentence for each problem.

1. The finish line for the race will be $5\frac{1}{2}$ meters long stretched across the road. Volunteers will be needed to watch each $\frac{1}{2}$ meter of the finish line to record the finishing time of each runner.

    How many volunteers will be needed?

2. Each runner in the race will be given a water bottle. Race organizers have $6\frac{1}{2}$ boxes of water bottles and there are 4 tables.

    If organizers put an equal number of boxes at each table, how many boxes will be put at each table?

3. Water stations for the runners will be set up every $1\frac{1}{9}$ kilometers in the 10-kilometer race.

    How many water stations will there be?

4. There will be 94 gallons of water available on race day.

    If each cup holds $\frac{1}{12}$ of a gallon of water, how many cups of water are available for runners?

LEARN

Solve Fraction Story Problems (B)

Practice Solving Division Problems

Write a number sentence for the problem. Then solve the problem.
Express your answer in simplest form.

1. Marion read 8 booklets in $\frac{2}{3}$ of an hour.

   At this rate, how many booklets can she read in an hour?

2. In $1\frac{1}{2}$ hours, fans for a baseball game filled $\frac{2}{3}$ of the seats in a stadium.

   At this rate, how many hours will it take to completely fill the stadium?

TRY IT

3. Glen's trip has taken $2\frac{1}{2}$ hours, and he is $\frac{5}{6}$ of the way there.
   How long will his trip take?

4. Dawn Marie's garden had an area of $4\frac{1}{2}$ square feet. It was $1\frac{2}{4}$ feet long.
   How wide was her garden?

Choose the answer. Be sure the answer is in simplest form.

5. The area of a path is 12 m². The width of the path is $1\frac{1}{8}$ m.
   How long is the path?

   A. $\frac{3}{32}$ m   B. $3\frac{5}{9}$ m   C. $10\frac{2}{3}$ m   D. $13\frac{1}{2}$ m

6. A race car can circle the racetrack $4\frac{1}{2}$ times in $4\frac{1}{4}$ minutes. How
   many times can the race car circle the track in 1 minute?

   A. $1\frac{1}{17}$ times   B. $1\frac{1}{16}$ times   C. $1\frac{1}{4}$ times   D. $1\frac{1}{2}$ times

T R Y   I T

Solve Fraction Story Problems (C)

Understand Fraction Story Problems

Worked Examples

You can write a number sentence to set up the solution for the following story problem:

- Avery and his father are making pizzas for a party. They have $7\frac{7}{8}$ cups of sauce. They want to put $1\frac{1}{6}$ cups of sauce on each pizza. How many pizzas can Avery and his father put sauce on?

PROBLEM 1 Write a number sentence that you can use to solve the story problem.

SOLUTION

1. Read the problem.

2. Decide what question needs to be answered. For this problem, you need to find how many pizzas Avery and his father can make with the given amount of sauce.

3. Decide what operation you need to use. For this problem, you need to use division to find the quotient of $7\frac{7}{8}$ divided by $1\frac{1}{6}$.

4. Write a number sentence that finds the quotient of the dividend $7\frac{7}{8}$ and the divisor $1\frac{1}{6}$.

ANSWER $7\frac{7}{8} \div 1\frac{1}{6} = ?$

PROBLEM 2 Solve the number sentence you wrote for Problem 1.

SOLUTION

1. Write the number sentence that solves the problem: $7\frac{7}{8} \div 1\frac{1}{6} = ?$

2. Change $7\frac{7}{8}$ and $1\frac{1}{6}$ to improper fractions: $\frac{63}{8} \div \frac{7}{6} = ?$

3. Change the division problem to a multiplication problem using the reciprocal of the divisor: $\frac{63}{8} \times \frac{6}{7} = ?$

4. Divide out the common factors. 7 is a common factor of 63 and 7. 2 is a common factor of 8 and 6: $\frac{9}{4} \times \frac{3}{1} = ?$

5 Multiply the numerators, and multiply the denominators: $\frac{27}{4}$

6 Change the improper fraction to a mixed number: $\frac{27}{4} = 6\frac{3}{4}$

7 $7\frac{7}{8} \div 1\frac{1}{6} = 6\frac{3}{4}$

ANSWER Avery and his father can put sauce on $6\frac{3}{4}$ pizzas.

You can write a number sentence to set up the solution for the following story problem:

- For dessert, Avery and his father are baking brownies. The recipe calls for $2\frac{5}{6}$ cups of flour. They want to make $1\frac{1}{2}$ times the recipe. How much flour should Avery and his father use?

PROBLEM 3 Write a number sentence that you can use to solve the story problem.

SOLUTION

1 Read the problem.

2 Decide what question needs to be answered. For this problem, you need to find how much flour Avery and his father should use to make $1\frac{1}{2}$ times the brownie recipe.

3 Decide what operation you need to use. For this problem, you need to use multiplication to find out what $2\frac{5}{6}$ times $1\frac{1}{2}$ equals.

4 Write a number sentence that finds the product of the factors $2\frac{5}{6}$ and $1\frac{1}{2}$.

ANSWER $2\frac{5}{6} \times 1\frac{1}{2} = ?$

PROBLEM 4 Solve the number sentence you wrote for Problem 3.

SOLUTION

1 Write the number sentence that solves the problem: $2\frac{5}{6} \times 1\frac{1}{2} = ?$

2 Change $2\frac{5}{6}$ and $1\frac{1}{2}$ to improper fractions: $\frac{17}{6} \times \frac{3}{2} = ?$

3 Divide out the common factors. 3 is a common factor of 6 and 3: $\frac{17}{2} \times \frac{1}{2} = ?$

4 Multiply the numerators, and multiply the denominators: $\frac{17}{4}$

5 Change the improper fraction to a mixed number: $\frac{17}{4} = 4\frac{1}{4}$

6 $2\frac{5}{6} \times 1\frac{1}{2} = 4\frac{1}{4}$

ANSWER Avery and his father should use $4\frac{1}{4}$ cups of flour.

Write a number sentence for each problem. Then go back and solve the problems.

1. The chef made lasagna this morning, and $\frac{7}{8}$ of a tray is left. If each serving is $\frac{1}{10}$ of a tray, how many servings can be served before the chef needs to make a new batch?

2. On the lunch menu, $\frac{4}{12}$ of the meals are sandwiches. Mayonnaise is on $\frac{7}{8}$ of the sandwiches. What fraction of meals on the menu have mayonnaise?

3. During lunch, $\frac{3}{10}$ of the customers order cheeseburgers and french fries. If there are 70 customers in the restaurant, how many customers order cheeseburgers and french fries?

4. A waiter had $\frac{3}{5}$ of an hour to set $9\frac{4}{5}$ more tables. If she spends the same amount of time setting each table, what fraction of each hour does she have to set each table?

5. Each day the chef prepares salads before the restaurant opens. The chef serves only full salads. If she uses $12\frac{3}{6}$ lb of cheese to make all the salads and puts $\frac{1}{12}$ lb on each one, how many salads does she prepare?

6. This is a recipe for baked potato soup. The chef needs to triple the recipe for a party. Calculate how much of each ingredient is needed to triple the recipe.

   $2\frac{1}{2}$ potatoes $\frac{3}{8}$ cup bacon

   $1\frac{1}{4}$ cups milk $\frac{1}{8}$ cup scallions

   $\frac{7}{8}$ cup cream $1\frac{2}{4}$ teaspoons pepper

   $\frac{1}{4}$ cup cheddar cheese $\frac{2}{3}$ teaspoon salt

LEARN

Solve Fraction Story Problems (C)

Multiply and Divide with Fractions

Memory Jogger

Follow these steps to solve multiplication story problems with fractions, whole numbers, and mixed numbers:

1. Read the problem.
2. Decide what question needs to be answered.
3. Decide what operation needs to be used.
4. Write the number sentence that solves the problem.
5. Change mixed numbers to improper fractions.
6. Change whole numbers to fractions with a denominator of 1.
7. Rewrite the problem, if needed.
8. Divide out the common factors, and rewrite the problem.
9. Multiply the numerators. Multiply the denominators. Write the product.
10. Simplify the product, if needed.
11. Use the product to answer the question in the problem.

Follow these steps to solve division story problems with fractions, whole numbers, and mixed numbers:

1. Read the problem.
2. Decide what question needs to be answered.
3. Decide what operation needs to be used.
4. Write the number sentence that solves the problem.
5. Change mixed numbers to improper fractions.
6. Change whole numbers to fractions with a denominator of 1.
7. Rewrite the problem, if needed.
8. Change the problem from division to multiplication by multiplying by the reciprocal of the divisor.
9. Divide out the common factors, and rewrite the problem.
10. Multiply the numerators. Multiply the denominators. Write the product.
11. Simplify the product, if needed.
12. Use the product to answer the question in the problem.

TRY IT

Write a number sentence for the problem. Then solve the problem.
Express your answer in simplest form.

1. Marie is $4\frac{1}{2}$ years old. Riva is $1\frac{1}{3}$ times older than Marie.
   How old is Riva?

2. Nancy has been traveling for $1\frac{1}{5}$ hours. She has covered $\frac{2}{3}$ of the
   distance of her trip. How long will her trip take?

Choose the answer. Be sure the answer is in simplest form.

3. The diameter on the wheels of a monster truck are $4\frac{1}{2}$ ft. Jeff is building a
   model $\frac{1}{3}$ the size of the monster truck. What diameter should he use for
   the wheels on his model?

   A. $1\frac{1}{3}$ ft
   B. $1\frac{1}{2}$ ft
   C. $2\frac{2}{3}$ ft
   D. $13\frac{1}{2}$ ft

4. An elephant at the zoo eats $3\frac{1}{2}$ tons of food in a year. If there are
   5 elephants in the zoo, how much food will they eat in a year?

   A. $15\frac{1}{2}$ tons
   B. $15\frac{2}{3}$ tons
   C. $17\frac{1}{2}$ tons
   D. $17\frac{2}{3}$ tons

5. It takes $\frac{1}{2}$ of a can of paint to cover $\frac{3}{4}$ of a wall. How many cans
   of paint will it take to cover the complete wall?

   A. $\frac{3}{8}$
   B. $\frac{2}{3}$
   C. $1\frac{1}{4}$
   D. $1\frac{1}{2}$

6. Debi can read $6\frac{3}{4}$ books in $2\frac{2}{8}$ weeks. How many books can she read
   in 1 week?

   A. $\frac{6}{8}$
   B. $1\frac{1}{3}$
   C. 3
   D. $15\frac{3}{16}$

Round Decimals Through Hundredths

Practice Rounding Decimals

Round the decimal number to the given place value.

1. 37.984 to the nearest hundredth

2. 311.65 to the nearest tenth

3. 43.652 to the nearest tenth

4. 123.712 to the nearest tenth

Solve by rounding to the given place value.

5. Pedro keeps a record of the amount of gasoline he buys for his lawn mowing service. His records show that he bought 138.93 gallons of gasoline this summer. About how many gallons of gas did Pedro buy this summer, rounded to the nearest tenth of a gallon?

6. The gas pump shows that Kelly bought 16.571 gallons of gas. About how many gallons of gas did Kelly buy, rounded to the nearest hundredth of a gallon?

Choose the answer.

7. What is 375.45 rounded to the nearest tenth?

   A. 370   B. 375.4

   C. 375.5   D. 380

8. What is 175.472 rounded to the nearest tenth?

   A. 175   B. 175.4

   C. 175.5   D. 180

9. What is 32.632 rounded to the nearest hundredth?

   A. 32.6   B. 32.63

   C. 32.7   D. 33

10. What is 76.925 rounded to the nearest whole number?

   A. 77   B. 76.93

   C. 76.9   D. 76

TRY IT

Estimate Decimal Sums, Differences (A)

Practice Estimating Decimal Sums

Solve.

1. Round each number to the nearest hundredth to estimate the sum of
   16.548 + 87.605.

   Round 16.548 to the nearest hundredth.

   Round 87.605 to the nearest hundredth.

   Estimate the sum.

2. Round each number to the nearest hundredth to estimate the sum of
   426.403 + 138.661.

   Round 426.403 to the nearest hundredth.

   Round 138.661 to the nearest hundredth.

   Estimate the sum.

3. Paula is keeping a record of the rainfall in her community for a science
   project. The rainfall was 8.493 inches last month and 3.788 inches this
   month. About how much rain fell in both months combined? Round
   each rainfall amount to the nearest hundredth to estimate the sum of
   8.493 + 3.788.

   Round 8.493 to the nearest hundredth.

   Round 3.788 to the nearest hundredth.

   Estimate the sum. About how much rain fell in both months combined?

Choose the answer.

4. Estimate the answer to 403.65 + 32.48
   by first rounding each number to the
   nearest tenth.

   A. 436.13   B. 436.2

   C. 436.7   D. 437

5. Estimate the answer to 43.91 + 72.69
   by first rounding each number to the
   nearest tenth.

   A. 110   B. 114.6

   C. 116.6   D. 118

TRY IT

Estimate Decimal Sums, Differences (B)

Practice Estimating Differences

Estimate by rounding each number to the nearest whole number and then subtracting.

1. 33.72 − 28.8

2. 987.23 − 85.22

Estimate by rounding each number to the nearest tenth and then subtracting.

3. 122.13 − 18.98

4. 856.32 − 76.78

Estimate by rounding each number to the nearest hundredth and then subtracting.

5. 360.727 − 89.852

6. 254.166 − 171.331

Choose the answer.

7. Estimate the answer by first rounding each number to the nearest tenth.

   151.23 − 25.67

   A. 125.7   B. 125

   C. 125.5   D. 126

8. Estimate the answer by first rounding each number to the nearest whole number.

   196.48 − 88.72

   A. 107   B. 107.7

   C. 107.8   D. 109

9. Estimate the answer by first rounding each number to the nearest hundredth.

   33.972 − 14.028

   A. 21.96   B. 21.94

   C. 19.96   D. 19.94

10. Estimate the answer by first rounding each number to the nearest tenth.

    294.32 − 198.32

    A. 100   B. 97

    C. 96   D. 90

TRY IT

Reasonable Answers and Decimal Problems

Practice Verifying Decimal Answers

Solve.

1. $98.4 + 23.65 =$ __?__

2. $77.632 - 9.3 =$ __?__

Estimate the answer by rounding each number to the nearest tenth and adding or subtracting. Read the exact answer given. Is the exact answer reasonable compared to the estimate? If not, calculate and write the correct exact answer.

3. A male giraffe at the zoo weighs 963.87 pounds. A female giraffe at the same zoo weighs 793.9 pounds. Sierra says the male giraffe weighs 884.48 pounds more than the female giraffe. Is her answer reasonable compared to your estimate?

4. When Zoe's puppy was born, it weighed 8.25 pounds. When it went for its one-year check-up, it weighed 43.8 more pounds. Zoe says her puppy now weighs 12.63 pounds. Is her answer reasonable compared to your estimate?

5. $897.26 + 392.65 = 1,192.9$

6. $61.35 - 35.86 = 97.21$

Estimate the answer by rounding each number to the nearest whole number and adding or subtracting. Read the exact answer given. Is the exact answer reasonable compared to the estimate? If not, calculate and write the correct exact answer.

7. Jason drove 12.5 km to the ballpark and then 1.825 km to the bank. What was the total distance he drove?

   Jason thought the answer was 30.75 km. Is his answer reasonable compared to your estimate?

8. Sophie rode her bike 16.135 km and walked 5.865 km. How much farther did she ride her bike than she walked?

   Sophie thought the answer was 22.000 km. Is her answer reasonable compared to your estimate?

TRY IT

Choose the answer.

9. $639.233 + 42.123 = ?$

   A. 681.356   B. 681.35

   C. 1671.356   D. 671.3

10. $123.43 - 3.4 = ?$

   A. 120.03   B. 120.43

   C. 121.03   D. 126.83

11. Jonathan said that $452.6 + 59.83$ equals 1,050.9. Is Jonathan's answer reasonable?

   A. Yes, Jonathan's answer is reasonable.

   B. No, the answer is about 500.

   C. No, the answer is about 600.

   D. No, the answer is about 900.

12. Greg said that $913.46 - 199.5$ equals 893.51. Is Greg's answer reasonable?

   A. Yes, Greg's answer is reasonable.

   B. No, the answer is about 700.

   C. No, the answer is about 1,000.

   D. No, the answer is about 1,100.

13. Walter solved this problem.

Richard had two pieces of molding. One piece measured 9.125 ft and the other measured 15.5 ft. How much molding did Richard have in all?

Walter thought the answer was 106.75 ft. Is Walter's answer reasonable?

   A. Yes, Walter's answer is reasonable.

   B. No, the answer is about 6 ft.

   C. No, the answer is about 25 ft.

   D. No, the answer is about 250 ft.

14. Claudia solved this problem.

On Wednesday it snowed 9.85 in. and on Thursday it snowed 5.325 in. How much more did it snow on Wednesday than Thursday?

Claudia thought the answer was 15.175 in. Is Claudia's answer reasonable?

   A. No, the answer is about 250 ft.

   B. No, the answer is about 5 in.

   C. No, the answer is about 10 in.

   D. No, the answer is about 14 in.

T R Y I T

Solve Story Problems with Decimals (A)

Add Decimals in Story Problems

Solve.

1. Jeff bought 15.5 m of red felt and 8.75 m of green felt.

   How much felt did Jeff buy?

2. Lola drove 16.125 km to the restaurant and then drove 4.9 km to the store.

   What is the total distance Lola drove?

Choose the answer.

3. Angie filled her gas tank twice in one week. She spent $29.23 the first time and $27.12 the second time.

   How much did Angie spend on gas that week?

   A. $46.35

   B. $56.35

   C. $57.35

   D. $67.35

4. On Monday, 1.123 in. of rain fell. On Tuesday, another 2.599 in. of rain fell.

   What was the total rainfall in the two days?

   A. 3.622 in.

   B. 3.712 in.

   C. 3.722 in.

   D. 3.723 in.

5. Joel spent $15.23 on a gift for his sister and $18.90 on a gift for his mother.

   How much did Joel spend altogether?

   A. $33.13

   B. $34.03

   C. $34.13

   D. $34.23

6. Freddy rode his bike 18.125 km on Saturday and 13.5 km on Sunday.

   How far did Freddy ride his bike in the two days?

   A. 21.625 km

   B. 31.175 km

   C. 31.130 km

   D. 31.625 km

7. Mary drove 32.875 km to the restaurant and then 8.225 km to the store.

   What is the total distance Mary drove?

   A. 40.000 km

   B. 41.000 km

   C. 40.100 km

   D. 41.100 km

8. Holly saved $62.50 of her allowance and her grandfather gave her an additional $50.

   How much money did Holly have?

   A. $63.00

   B. $67.50

   C. $112.50

   D. $113.00

TRY IT

Solve Story Problems with Decimals (B)

Subtract Decimals in Story Problems

Solve.

1. Lisa weighs 42.135 kg and Amanda weighs 41.585 kg. How much more does Lisa weigh than Amanda?

2. The new world record for distance traveled on a bicycle in 1 hour is 56.375 km. The old record was 51.151 km. How much longer is the new world record than the old one?

3. Charlie spent $32.12 on new clothes. He paid with a $50 bill. How much change did he get back?

4. The Willot family owns two Great Dane dogs. The male weighs 150.366 pounds. The female weighs 135.358 pounds. How many more pounds does the male dog weigh than the female dog?

Choose the answer.

5. In 2008, the world record for the men's outdoor shot put was 23.12 m. The world record for the women's outdoor shot put was 22.63 m. How much longer is the men's record than the women's record?

   A. 0.49 m

   B. 1.49 m

   C. 1.51 m

   D. 1.59 m

6. William ran the 100-yard dash in 13.12 seconds. His time was 2.84 seconds slower than the school record. What was the school record?

   A. 10.28 seconds

   B. 10.38 seconds

   C. 11.28 seconds

   D. 15.96 seconds

7. Megan paid $6.49 for 2 gallons of milk. Rosie paid $5.89 for 2 gallons of milk. How much more did Megan pay than Rosie?

   A. $0.60

   B. $0.70

   C. $0.80

   D. $1.60

8. When Emily was born, she weighed 8.2 pounds. In two months, she weighed 10.15 pounds. How much weight did Emily gain in her first two months?

   A. 1.05 pounds

   B. 1.95 pounds

   C. 2.05 pounds

   D. 18.35 pounds

TRY IT

Estimate Decimal Products, Quotients (A)

Practice Estimating Products

Round each factor to the given place to estimate the product.

1. 32.739 × 826.301
    Round factors to the nearest ten.

2. 13.728 × 3.9
    Round factors to the nearest whole number.

Use friendly numbers to estimate the product. Explain your answer.

3. 0.217 × 0.352

4. 0.721 × 3.88

5. 71.62 × 0.51

6. 151.22 × 1.002

7. 5,498.021 × 9.87

Estimate the product. Choose the answer.

8. Use friendly numbers to estimate the product of 21.21 × 999.201.

    A. 20,000   B. 2,000   C. 200   D. 20

9. Rhonda was multiplying 6.3 by 0.1. Which statement is true about the product?

    A. It will be greater than 6.3.

    B. It will be equal to 6.3.

    C. It will be less than 6.3.

10. Joan was multiplying 9.1 by 0.001. Which statement is true about the product?

    A. It will be more than 9.0.   B. It will be more than 0.90.

    C. It will be more than 0.090.   D. It will be more than 0.0090.

Challenge Question

Round each factor to the nearest hundredth to estimate the product.

11. 31.614 × 3.497

TRY IT

Estimate Decimal Products, Quotients (B)

Practice Estimating Quotients

Estimate the quotient. Explain your answer.

1. $5.253 \div 0.249$

2. $352.3 \div 0.53$

3. $4,512.091 \div 0.11$

4. $9,032.87 \div 44.912$

Use friendly numbers to round the dividend and divisor.
Then divide to find the estimated quotient. Choose the answer.

5. $9.59 \div 0.24$

    A. 0.2   B. 2.8

    C. 6.1   D. 40

6. $76.12 \div 4.901$

    A. 1.5   B. 15

    C. 150   D. 1,500

Round the dividend and divisor to the nearest tenth.
Then divide to find the estimated quotient. Choose the answer.

7. $8.07 \div 0.87$

    A. 0.9   B. 8.1

    C. 9   D. 81

8. $8.39 \div 1.22$

    A. 0.013   B. 0.07

    C. 7   D. 10

Round the dividend and divisor to the nearest whole number.
Then divide to find the estimated quotient. Choose the answer.

9. $719.711 \div 8.75$

    A. 8,000   B. 800   C. 80   D. 8

Choose the answer.

10. Deborah was dividing 10.3 by 0.1. Which statement is true about the quotient?

    A. It will be equal to 10.3.

    B. It will be greater than 10.3.

    C. It will be less than 10.3.

11. Joan was dividing 0.32 by 0.001. Which statement is true about the quotient?

    A. It will be less than 3,000.

    B. It will be less than 30.0.

    C. It will be less than 0.030.

    D. It will be less than 0.0030.

TRY IT

Estimate Decimal Products, Quotients (C)

Practice Estimating Decimal Answers

Use the given strategy to estimate the product or quotient. Explain your answer.

1. 0.471×6.379
   Round factors to the nearest tenth.

2. $0.893 \div 3.102$
   Round the dividend and divisor to friendly numbers.

Estimate the product or quotient. Choose the answer.

3. 3.09×304.87

   A. 9.0   B. 9.9

   C. 90   D. 900

4. 78.101×4.912

   A. 0.4   B. 4.0

   C. 40   D. 400

5. $102.02 \div 4.011$

   A. 25   B. 250

   C. 2,500   D. 25,000

6. $456,021.011 \div 10.002$

   A. 45,000   B. 4,500

   C. 450   D. 45

Choose the answer.

7. Patrick was multiplying 0.94 by 0.1. Which statement is true about the product?

   A. It will be equal to 0.94.

   B. It will be less than 0.94.

   C. It will be greater than 0.94.

8. Deb was dividing 14.1 by 0.01. Which statement is true about the quotient?

   A. It will be equal to 14.1.

   B. It will be greater than 14.1.

   C. It will be less than 14.1.

9. Julie was multiplying 17.2 by 0.001. Which statement is true about the product?

   A. It will be more than 15.

   B. It will be more than 1.5.

   C. It will be more than 0.15.

   D. It will be more than 0.015.

10. Edgar was dividing 0.64 by 0.001. Which statement is true about the quotient?

    A. It will be less than 6,000.

    B. It will be less than 0.060.

    C. It will be less than 60.0.

    D. It will be less than 0.0060.

Challenge Question

Solve.

11. If the product of $541,392 \times 7.51 = 4,065,853.92$, what is the product of 54.1392×75.1?

TRY IT

Multiply and Divide Decimals (A)

Multiply a Whole Number by a Decimal

Worked Examples

You can use a step-by-step approach, or an algorithm, to find the product of a decimal number and a whole number.

PROBLEM 1 $0.9 \times 3 = ?$

SOLUTION Follow the steps to multiply a number in tenths by a whole number.

1 Write the problem vertically. ⟶

$$\begin{array}{r} 0.9 \\ \times\ 3 \\ \hline \end{array}$$

2 Multiply the digits. The result is actually 27 tenths, since you have 3 groups of 9 tenths. ⟶

$$\begin{array}{r} 0.9 \\ \times\ 3 \\ \hline 27 \end{array}$$

3 Place the decimal point in your answer according to its place value. Because you multiplied tenths by ones, the answer is expressed as tenths. Check the place value by using fractions to multiply. ⟶

$$\begin{array}{r} 0.9 \\ \times\ 3 \\ \hline 2.7 \end{array}$$

4 Use fractions to make sure tenths are correct for expressing the answer.

$$\frac{9}{10} \times 3 = \frac{9}{10} \times \frac{3}{1} = \frac{27}{10} = 2\frac{7}{10}$$

ANSWER $0.9 \times 3 = 2.7$

PROBLEM 2 $2 \times 0.87 = ?$

SOLUTION Follow the steps to multiply a whole number by a number in hundredths.

1 Write the problem vertically. ⟶

$$\begin{array}{r} 0.87 \\ \times\ \ 2 \\ \hline \end{array}$$

2 Multiply the digits. The result is actually 174 hundredths, since you have 2 groups of 87 hundredths. ⟶

$$\begin{array}{r} {\scriptstyle 1\ 1} \\ 0.87 \\ \times\ \ 2 \\ \hline 174 \end{array}$$

L E A R N

3 Place the decimal point in your answer according to its place value. ⟶
Because you multiplied hundredths by ones, the answer is expressed
as hundredths. Check the place value by using fractions to multiply.

$$\begin{array}{r} \overset{1\ \ 1}{0.87} \\ \times\ \ 2 \\ \hline 1.74 \end{array}$$

4 Use fractions to make sure hundredths are correct for expressing the answer.

$$2 \times \frac{87}{100} = \frac{2}{1} \times \frac{87}{100} = \frac{174}{100} = 1\frac{74}{100}$$

ANSWER $2 \times 0.87 = 1.74$

PROBLEM 3 $5.231 \times 3 = ?$

SOLUTION Follow the steps to multiply a number in thousandths by a
whole number.

1 Write the problem vertically. ⟶

$$\begin{array}{r} 5.231 \\ \times\ \ \ \ 3 \\ \hline \end{array}$$

2 Multiply the digits. The result is actually 15,693 thousandths, since ⟶
you have 3 groups of 5 and 231 thousandths.

$$\begin{array}{r} 5.231 \\ \times\ \ \ \ 3 \\ \hline 15693 \end{array}$$

3 Place the decimal point in your answer according to its place value. ⟶
Because you multiplied thousandths by ones, the answer is expressed as
thousandths.

$$\begin{array}{r} 5.231 \\ \times\ \ \ \ 3 \\ \hline 15.693 \end{array}$$

ANSWER $5.231 \times 3 = 15.693$

Estimate the product. Find the exact answer using an algorithm. Compare the
exact answer to the estimated answer to see if the exact answer is reasonable.

1. $2 \times 1.2 = ?$

2. $3 \times 0.33 = ?$

LEARN

Multiply and Divide Decimals (A)

Multiply a Decimal by a Decimal

Worked Examples

You can use a step-by-step approach, or an algorithm, to find the product of two decimal numbers.

PROBLEM 1 $0.8 \times 0.4 = ?$

SOLUTION Follow the steps to multiply two numbers in tenths.

1 Write the problem vertically.

$$\begin{array}{r} 0.8 \\ \times\, 0.4 \\ \hline \end{array}$$

2 Multiply the digits. The result is actually 32 hundredths, since you have tenths multiplied by tenths.

$$\left(\frac{1}{10} \times \frac{1}{10} = \frac{1}{100}\right)$$

$$\begin{array}{r} 0.8 \\ \times\, 0.4 \\ \hline 32 \end{array}$$

3 Place the decimal point in your answer according to its place value. Because tenths multiplied by tenths is hundredths, the number of decimal places to the right of the decimal would be two places. Check the place value by using fractions to multiply.

$$\begin{array}{r} 0.8 \\ \times\, 0.4 \\ \hline 0.32 \end{array}$$

4 Use fractions to make sure hundredths are correct for expressing the answer.

$$\frac{8}{10} \times \frac{4}{10} = \frac{32}{100}$$

ANSWER $0.8 \times 0.4 = 0.32$

PROBLEM 2 $4.08 \times 0.25 = ?$

SOLUTION Follow the steps to multiply two numbers in hundredths.

1 Write the problem vertically.

$$\begin{array}{r} 4.08 \\ \times\, 0.25 \\ \hline \end{array}$$

2 Multiply the digits. The result is actually 10,200 ten thousandths, since you have hundredths multiplied by hundredths.

$$\left(\frac{1}{100} \times \frac{1}{100} = \frac{1}{10,000}\right)$$

$$\begin{array}{r} \overset{1}{\cancel{4}} \quad \\ 4.08 \\ \times\, 0.25 \\ \hline 2040 \\ +\,8160 \\ \hline 10200 \end{array}$$

81

L E A R N

3 Place the decimal point in your answer according to its place value. Because hundredths multiplied by hundredths is ten thousandths, the number of decimal places to the right of the decimal would be four places. Check the place value by using fractions to multiply.

$$\overset{1}{\cancel{4}}.08$$
$$\times 0.25$$
$$\overline{2040}$$
$$+8160$$
$$\overline{1.0200}$$

This answer is the same as 1.02.

4 Use fractions to make sure ten thousandths, simplified to hundredths, are correct for expressing the answer.

$$4\frac{8}{100} \times \frac{25}{100} = \frac{408}{100} \times \frac{25}{100} = \frac{10,200}{10,000} = 1\frac{200}{10,000} = 1\frac{2}{100}$$

ANSWER $4.08 \times 0.25 = 1.02$

PROBLEM 3 $0.75 \times 7.808 = ?$

SOLUTION Follow the steps to multiply a number in hundredths by a number in thousandths.

1 Write the problem vertically.

$$7.808$$
$$\times 0.75$$

2 Multiply the digits. The result is actually 585,600 hundred thousandths, since you have hundredths multiplied by thousandths.

$$\frac{1}{100} \times \frac{1}{1,000} = \frac{1}{100,000}$$

$$\overset{5}{\cancel{4}}\ \overset{5}{\cancel{4}}$$
$$7.808$$
$$\times 0.75$$
$$\overline{39040}$$
$$+546560$$
$$\overline{585600}$$

3 Place the decimal point in your answer according to its place value. Because hundredths multiplied by thousandths is hundred thousandths, the number of decimal places to the right of the decimal would be five places.

$$\overset{5}{\cancel{4}}\ \overset{5}{\cancel{4}}$$
$$7.808$$
$$\times 0.75$$
$$\overline{39040}$$
$$+546560$$
$$\overline{5.85600}$$

This answer is the same as 5.856.

ANSWER $0.75 \times 7.808 = 5.686$

Estimate the product. Find the exact answer by using an algorithm. Compare the exact answer to the estimated answer to see if the exact answer is reasonable.

1. $0.9 \times 4.04 = ?$

2. $5.05 \times 2.22 = ?$

3. $0.025 \times 0.52 = ?$

Multiply and Divide Decimals (A)

Practice Multiplying Decimals

Multiply. Give the exact answer.

1. $7.7 \times 0.3 = \underline{\ ?\ }$

2. $0.93 \times 1.8 = \underline{\ ?\ }$

3. $2.22 \times 4.05 = \underline{\ ?\ }$

4. $0.02 \times 10,003.9 = \underline{\ ?\ }$

5. $100.8 \times 300.6 = \underline{\ ?\ }$

6. $887.9 \times 3.9 = \underline{\ ?\ }$

7. $3.82 \times 14.6 = \underline{\ ?\ }$

Estimate the product by rounding the factors to the nearest whole number. Then find the exact answer.

8. $5.4 \times 7 = ?$

Choose the answer.

9. $0.34 \times 44.2 = ?$

   A. 15.028
   B. 150.28
   C. 1,502.8
   D. 15,028

10. $1.9 \times 1,982.34 = ?$

   A. 3,766,446
   B. 376,644.6
   C. 37,664.46
   D. 3,766.446

Challenge Question

Multiply. Give the exact answer.

11. $7.005 \times 3.06 = \underline{\ ?\ }$

T R Y   I T

Multiply and Divide Decimals (B)

Divide Whole Numbers and Decimals

Worked Examples

You can use a step-by-step approach, or algorithm, to divide a decimal number by a whole number and to divide a whole number by a decimal number.

PROBLEM 1 $1.8 \div 2 = ?$

SOLUTION   Follow the steps to divide a number in tenths by a whole number.

1   Use the long-division symbol to write the problem. $\longrightarrow$ $2\overline{)1.8}$
Dividing 1.8 by 2 is similar to dividing a whole number by 2.

2   Line up all place values in the dividend and quotient. The 9 in $\longrightarrow$ $2\overline{)1.8}^{\,0.9}$
the quotient should be placed above the 8. You can see that
1.8 divided by 2 is 0.9.

3   Use fractions to make sure tenths are correct for expressing the answer.

$$1\frac{8}{10} \div 2 = \frac{18}{10} \div \frac{2}{1} = \frac{\overset{9}{\cancel{18}}}{10} \times \frac{1}{\underset{1}{\cancel{2}}} = \frac{9}{10}$$

ANSWER $1.8 \div 2 = 0.9$

PROBLEM 2 $0.21 \div 7 = ?$

SOLUTION   Follow the steps to divide a number in hundredths by a whole number.

1   Use the long-division symbol to write the problem. $\longrightarrow$ $7\overline{)0.21}$
Dividing 0.21 by 7 is similar to dividing a whole number by 7.
Lining up place values is important here, too.

2   Line up all place values in the dividend and quotient. The 3 $\longrightarrow$ $7\overline{)0.21}^{\,0.03}$
in the quotient needs to be above the 1, so if you place a 0
between the decimal point and the 3, you create the two places
that are needed.

3   Use fractions to make sure hundredths are correct for expressing the answer.

$$\frac{21}{100} \div 7 = \frac{21}{100} \div \frac{7}{1} = \frac{\overset{3}{\cancel{21}}}{100} \times \frac{1}{\underset{1}{\cancel{7}}} = \frac{3}{100}$$

ANSWER $0.21 \div 7 = 0.03$

PROBLEM 3 $6 \div 1.2 = ?$

SOLUTION Follow the steps to divide a whole number by a number in tenths.

1 Use the long-division symbol to write the problem. Dividing by a decimal number is easier if you multiply to change the divisor into a whole number. Multiply the dividend by the same number. Look at the problem as a fraction, even though it looks a little strange: $\frac{6.0}{1.2}$. Create an equivalent fraction so that 1.2 becomes a whole number. Multiply 1.2 by 10 to get 12. Both the numerator and denominator must be multiplied by the same value. Multiply 6.0 by 10.

$$\frac{6.0}{1.2} \times \frac{10}{10} = \frac{60}{12}$$

$$1.2\overline{)6.0}$$

2 Line up all place values in the dividend and quotient, so the 5 in the quotient should be placed above the 0. You can see that $60 \div 12 = 5$. Because $60 \div 12$ is equivalent to $6.0 \div 1.2$, the quotient of $6.0 \div 1.2$ is also 5.

$$\overset{5}{12\overline{)60}}$$

3 Use fractions to make sure that a whole number is correct for expressing the answer.

$$6.0 \div 1.2 = \frac{6}{1} \div 1\frac{2}{10} = 6 \div \frac{12}{10} = \frac{\overset{1}{\cancel{6}}}{1} \times \frac{10}{\underset{2}{\cancel{12}}} = \frac{10}{2} = 5$$

ANSWER $6 \div 1.2 = 5$

PROBLEM 4 $20 \div 1.25 = ?$

SOLUTION Follow the steps to divide a whole number by a number in hundredths.

1 Use the long-division symbol to write the problem. Multiply to change the divisor into a whole number. Multiply the dividend by the same number. Look at the problem as a fraction: $\frac{20}{1.25}$. Multiply the numerator and denominator by 1 in the form of $\frac{100}{100}$. Change your original fraction to an equivalent fraction that will be easier for your division problem.

$$1.25\overline{)20}$$

$$\frac{20}{1.25} \times \frac{100}{100} = \frac{2,000}{125}$$

2 Line up all place values in the dividend and quotient. You can see that $2,000 \div 125 = 16$. Because $2,000 \div 125$ is equivalent to $20 \div 1.25$, the quotient of $20 \div 1.25$ is also 16.

ANSWER $20 \div 1.25 = 16$

$$\begin{array}{r} 16 \\ 125\overline{)2,000} \\ -1,250 \\ \hline 750 \\ -750 \\ \hline 0 \end{array}$$

LEARN

Estimate the quotient. Find the exact answer by using an algorithm. Compare the exact answer to the estimated answer to see if the exact answer is reasonable.

1. $0.25 \div 5 = ?$

2. $6 \div 1.5 = ?$

LEARN

Multiply and Divide Decimals (B)

Divide a Decimal by a Decimal

You can use a step-by-step approach, or algorithm, to divide a decimal number by a decimal number.

PROBLEM $1.344 \div 0.12 = ?$

SOLUTION Follow the steps to divide a number in thousandths by a number in hundredths.

1 Look at the problem as a fraction. $\longrightarrow \dfrac{1.344}{0.12}$

2 Simplify the division by making the divisor a whole number. Multiply the divisor by 100 to change 0.12 to the whole number 12. Multiply the dividend by 100 to change 1.344 to 134.4. $\longrightarrow \dfrac{1.344}{0.12} \times \dfrac{100}{100} = \dfrac{134.4}{12}$

3 Use the long-division symbol to write the new division problem. $\longrightarrow 12\overline{)134.4}$

4 Line up all place values in the dividend and quotient, so you can see that the quotient of $134.4 \div 12$ is 11.2. Because $134.4 \div 12$ is equivalent to $1.344 \div 0.12$, the quotient of $1.344 \div 0.12$ is also 11.2.

$$
\begin{array}{r}
11.2 \\
12\overline{)134.4} \\
-12 \\
\hline
14 \\
-12 \\
\hline
24 \\
-24 \\
\hline
0
\end{array}
$$

ANSWER $1.344 \div 0.12 = 11.2$

Estimate the quotient. Find the exact answer by using an algorithm. Compare the exact answer to the estimated answer to see if the exact answer is reasonable.

1. $17.5 \div 3.5 = ?$

2. $1.12 \div 0.8 = ?$

3. $3.84 \div 2.4 = ?$

L E A R N

Multiply and Divide Decimals (B)

Practice Dividing Decimals

Estimate the quotient by using friendly numbers.
Then find the exact answer.

1. $14.7 \div 7 = ?$

Divide. Give the exact answer.

2. $5.84 \div 0.8 = \underline{\ ?\ }$

3. $7.2 \div 0.9 = \underline{\ ?\ }$

4. $4.48 \div 3.2 = \underline{\ ?\ }$

5. $99.88 \div 0.001 = \underline{\ ?\ }$

6. $99.891 \div 0.022 = \underline{\ ?\ }$

7. $4{,}556.29 \div 99.7 = \underline{\ ?\ }$

8. $0.017 \div 0.002 = \underline{\ ?\ }$

9. $89{,}997 \div 0.5 = \underline{\ ?\ }$

Choose the answer.

10. $4{,}568.629 \div 999.7 = ?$

    A. 4,570   B. 457   C. 45.7   D. 4.57

Challenge Question

Use the order of operations to find the answer.

11. $(1.2 \times 1.8) \div 0.6 = \underline{\ ?\ }$

TRY IT

Multiply and Divide Decimals (C)

Decimal Quotients

Worked Examples

You can use a step-by-step approach, or an algorithm, to divide a whole number by a greater whole number, resulting in a decimal quotient.

PROBLEM 1 $3 \div 10 = ?$

SOLUTION Follow the steps to divide a whole number by a greater whole number.

1. Use the long-division symbol to write the problem. ⟶ $10\overline{)3}$

2. Show the dividend as a decimal number with as many zeros as ⟶ $10\overline{)3.0}$
   needed to make the division work out evenly. Add one zero after
   the decimal point in this dividend.

3. Line up all place values in the dividend and quotient. The 3 in the ⟶ $10\overline{)3.0}^{\ 0.3}$
   quotient should be placed above the zero in 3.0.

4. Use fractions to make sure tenths are correct for expressing the answer.
   Recall that the fraction bar can also be used as a division symbol, so
   $3 \div 10$ is the same as $\frac{3}{10}$, 3 tenths, and 0.3.

ANSWER $3 \div 10 = 0.3$

PROBLEM 2 $6 \div 12 = ?$

SOLUTION Follow the steps to divide another whole number by a
greater whole number, resulting in a decimal quotient.

1. Use the long-division symbol to write the problem. ⟶ $12\overline{)6}$

2. Show the dividend as a decimal number with as many zeros as ⟶ $12\overline{)6.0}$
   needed to make the division work out evenly. Add one zero after
   the decimal point in this dividend.

3. Line up all place values in the dividend and quotient. The 5 in the ⟶ $12\overline{)6.0}^{\ 0.5}$
   quotient should be placed above the zero in 6.0.

L E A R N

4 Use fractions to make sure tenths are correct for expressing the answer. Recall that the fraction bar can also be used as a division symbol, so $6 \div 12$ is the same as $\frac{6}{12}$, which simplifies to $\frac{1}{2}$ or 0.5.

ANSWER $6 \div 12 = 0.5$

PROBLEM 3 $6 \div 25 = ?$

SOLUTION Follow the steps to divide another whole number by a greater whole number, resulting in a decimal quotient.

1 Use the long-division symbol to write the problem. ⟶ $25\overline{)6}$

2 Show the dividend as a decimal number with as many zeros as ⟶ $25\overline{)6.00}$ needed to make the division work out evenly. Add two zeros after the decimal point in this dividend.

3 Line up all place values in the dividend and quotient. The 2 in the ⟶ quotient should be placed above the zero in the tenths place in 6.00, and the 4 in the quotient should be placed above the zero in the hundredths place in 6.00.

$$\begin{array}{r} 0.24 \\ 25\overline{)6.00} \\ -5.00 \\ \hline 1.00 \\ -1.00 \\ \hline 0 \end{array}$$

4 Use fractions to make sure hundredths are correct for expressing the answer. Recall that the fraction bar can also be used as a division symbol, so $6 \div 25$ is the same as $\frac{6}{25}$, which is the same as 0.24.

ANSWER $6 \div 25 = 0.24$

Use an algorithm to divide.

1. $9 \div 15 = ?$

2. $8 \div 32 = ?$

3. $7 \div 20 = ?$

LEARN

Multiply and Divide Decimals (C)

Practice Multiplying and Dividing

Use $2.2 \div 1.25 = ?$ for Problems 1–4.

1. Round the dividend and the divisor to the nearest whole number. Write a number sentence to estimate the quotient. Find the estimated quotient.

2. Calculate the exact quotient.

3. Use multiplication to check the exact quotient.

4. Use the estimate to explain how you know if the exact quotient is reasonable.

Write a number sentence and estimate the product. Then find the exact product. Explain how you know if the exact answer is reasonable.

5. $6 \times 5.43 = ?$

6. $0.14 \times 0.6 = ?$

Write a number sentence and estimate the quotient. Then find the exact quotient. Explain how you know if the exact answer is reasonable.

7. $14 \div 25 = ?$

8. $7.2 \div 6 = ?$

Solve.

9. $4.5 \times 2.55 = \underline{\ ?\ }$

10. $0.19 \times 201.5 = \underline{\ ?\ }$

11. $0.75 \div 375 = \underline{\ ?\ }$

12. $4.08 \div 0.16 = \underline{\ ?\ }$

13. $117.6 \div 2.1 = \underline{\ ?\ }$

Choose the answer.

14. $93.7 \times 8.1 = ?$

   A. 7.5897   B. 75.897

   C. 758.97   D. 7,589.7

15. $345.56 \div 5.3 = ?$

   A. 6,520   B. 652

   C. 65.2   D. 6.52

TRY IT

Compute Decimal Story Problems (A)

Bicycle Race Decimal Story Problems

Worked Examples

You can write a number sentence with decimal numbers and solve it to find the answer to the following story problem.

- A book about bicycle racing costs $12.95. What is the cost of 4 books?

PROBLEM 1 Write a number sentence that you can use to solve the story problem.

SOLUTION

1 Read the problem.

2 Decide what question needs to be answered. For this problem, you need to find the cost of 4 books that cost $12.95 each.

3 Decide what operation to use. For this problem, you need to use multiplication to find what $12.95 per book for 4 books equals.

4 Write a number sentence that finds the product of the factors 12.95 and 4.

ANSWER $12.95 \times 4 = ?$

PROBLEM 2 Solve the number sentence you wrote for Problem 1. Answer the question in a complete sentence.

SOLUTION

1 Write the number sentence that solves the problem. $\longrightarrow$ $12.95 \times 4 = ?$

2 Write the problem vertically. Use a step-by-step process to solve the problem.

$$\longrightarrow \begin{array}{r} 12.95 \\ \times \quad 4 \\ \hline \end{array}$$

3 Multiply. You are multiplying hundredths by a whole number, so the answer is in hundredths.

$$\longrightarrow \begin{array}{r} {\scriptstyle 1\,3\,2} \\ 12.95 \\ \times \quad 4 \\ \hline 51.80 \end{array}$$

ANSWER The cost of 4 books on bicycle racing is $51.80.

L E A R N

Write a multiplication number sentence. Solve. Answer the question in a complete sentence.

1. The Tour with Us bicycle race takes place over 3 days. If cyclists ride 23.76 kilometers a day, how many kilometers long is the race?

2. One kilometer is equal to 0.62 of a mile. If a race is 134.4 kilometers, how many miles is it equivalent to?

3. Along the race route, vendors sell T-shirts for $11.55. How much will it cost to buy 8 T-shirts?

4. Vendors also have sun visors for $5.15. How much will it cost to buy 20 sun visors?

5. On average, a cyclist can bike 24 kilometers in an hour. How many kilometers will he bike in 8.6 hours?

6. The average weight of a bicycle is 27.8 pounds. What is the combined weight of 11 bicycles?

7. The Race with Me bicycle race takes place over 8 days. If cyclists ride 45.85 kilometers a day, how many kilometers long is the race?

8. One meter is equal to 3.28 feet. If a time trial is 19.6 meters long, how many feet is it equivalent to?

9. At the end of the race, vendors sell T-shirts with the winner's name on them. If each T-shirts costs $16.30, how much will 6 T-shirts cost?

10. The leader of the race is averaging 28.3 kilometers an hour. If she rides at the same speed for the entire time, how many kilometers will she bike in 5.7 hours?

LEARN

Compute Decimal Story Problems (B)

Picnic Decimal Story Problems

Worked Examples

You can write a number sentence with decimal numbers and solve it to find the answer to the following story problem.

- Children at a picnic sang the same song 4 times in a row. They sang for a total of 10.4 minutes. If singing the song takes the same number of minutes each time, how many minutes does it take to sing the song?

PROBLEM 1 Write a number sentence that you can use to solve the story problem.

SOLUTION

1 Read the problem.

2 Decide what question needs to be answered. For this problem, you need to find the number of minutes children would spend if they sang the song one time.

3 Decide what operation to use. For this problem, you need to use division to find the quotient of 10.4 minutes divided by 4 times.

4 Write a number sentence that finds the quotient of the dividend 10.4 and the divisor 4.

ANSWER $10.4 \div 4 = ?$

PROBLEM 2 Solve the number sentence you wrote for Problem 1.
Answer the question in a complete sentence.

SOLUTION

1 Write the number sentence that solves the problem. $\longrightarrow$ $10.4 \div 4 = ?$

2 Use the long-division symbol to write the problem. $\longrightarrow$ $4 \overline{)10.4}$
Use a step-by-step process to solve the problem.

3 Divide. You are dividing tenths by a whole number, so the ⟶ answer is in tenths.

$$\begin{array}{r} 2.6 \\ 4)\overline{10.4} \\ -8.0 \\ \hline 2.4 \\ -2.4 \\ \hline 0 \end{array}$$

ANSWER Singing the song one time takes 2.6 minutes.

Write a division number sentence. Solve. Answer the question in a complete sentece.

1. At the annual spring picnic, 15 people barbecued a total of 4.35 pounds of chicken. They each ate the same amount of chicken. How much barbecued chicken did each person eat?

2. Dana and his family drove 54.75 miles to a picnic. They traveled 36.5 miles each hour. How many hours did it take them to drive to the picnic?

3. Teresa paid $6.48 for a package of 24 paper plates. What is the price of 1 paper plate?

4. Ed made 3 pounds of tossed green salad for a picnic. When they sat down to eat, 12 people shared the salad equally. How many pounds of salad did each person have?

5. Natasha bought propane to use in the barbecue at a picnic. She paid $44.16 and bought 9.6 pounds. How much did the propane cost per pound?

6. A group of children played 5 games for a total of 2.75 hours at a picnic. Each game lasted the same amount of time. How many hours did each game last?

7. A family went on a boat ride at a picnic. The boat traveled 27.5 miles in 1.25 hours. If the boat travels at the same speed for the entire trip, how many miles did the boat travel in 1 hour?

8. The picnic tables at a park are all the same length. When 4 tables are pushed together, they form a table that measures 7.2 meters long. What is the length of 1 picnic table?

9. Rachel brought 76.5 ounces of grape juice to a picnic. She poured the juice into cups that hold 8.5 ounces each. How many cups of juice did Rachel fill?

10. Mrs. Gomez bought 3 picnic baskets for a total of $41.97. Each picnic basket cost the same price. How much did Mrs. Gomez pay for each picnic basket?

L E A R N

Compute Decimal Story Problems (C)

More Camping Trip Story Problems

Worked Examples

You can write a number sentence with decimal numbers and solve it to find the answer to the following story problem.

- Melissa drove 45.5 kilometers each hour for 6.25 hours to get to the campsite. How many kilometers did Melissa drive in all?

PROBLEM 1 Write a number sentence that you can use to solve the story problem.

SOLUTION

1 Read the problem.

2 Decide what question needs to be answered. For this problem, you need to find how many kilometers Melissa drove in 6.25 hours at a speed of 45.5 kilometers each hour.

3 Decide what operation to use. For this problem, you need to use multiplication to find the product of 6.25 and 45.5.

4 Write a number sentence that finds the product of the factors 6.25 and 45.5.

ANSWER $45.5 \times 6.25 = ?$

PROBLEM 2 Solve the number sentence you wrote for Problem 1. Answer the question in a complete sentence.

SOLUTION

1 Write the number sentence that solves the problem. ⟶ $45.5 \times 6.25 = ?$

2 Write the problem vertically. Use a step-by-step process to solve the problem. ⟶

$$
\begin{array}{r}
45.5 \\
\times\ 6.25 \\
\hline
2275 \\
9100 \\
+\ 273000 \\
\hline
284.375
\end{array}
$$

ANSWER Melissa drove 284.375 kilometers in all.

You can write a number sentence with decimal numbers and solve it to find the answer to the following story problem.

- Some of the campers drove 34.8 miles to see a waterfall. They saw a road sign every 6.96 miles. How many road signs did they see?

PROBLEM 3 Write a number sentence that you can use to solve this story problem.

SOLUTION

1. Read the problem.

2. Decide what question needs to be answered. For this problem, you need to find out how many road signs the campers saw if they saw a sign every 6.96 miles for 34.8 miles.

3. Decide what operation you need to use. For this problem, you need to use division to find the quotient of 34.8 divided by 6.96.

4. Write a number sentence that finds the quotient of 34.8 and the divisor 6.96.

ANSWER $34.8 \div 6.96 = ?$

PROBLEM 4 Solve the number sentence you wrote for Problem 3. Answer the question in a complete sentence.

SOLUTION

1. Write the number sentence that solves this problem. ⟶ $34.8 \div 6.96 = ?$

2. Use the long-division symbol to write the problem. ⟶ $6.96\overline{)34.8}$
   Use a step-by-step process to solve the problem.

3. Divide. You are dividing tenths by hundredths, ⟶ $6.96\overline{)34.8} = 696\overline{)3480.0}$
   so the answer is in tenths.

$$\begin{array}{r} 5.0 \\ 696\overline{)3480.0} \\ -3480.0 \\ \hline 0 \end{array}$$

ANSWER The campers saw 5 road signs.

Write a multiplication or division number sentence. Solve.
Write the answer in a complete sentence.

1. It costs $42.95 to stay 1 night in a cabin at a campground. What is the cost of staying in the cabin for 5 nights?

2. Dean and his friends drove 37.3 kilometers each hour for 5.25 hours to get from the ranger station to the campsite by the lake. How many kilometers did Dean and his friends drive in all?

LEARN

3. The distance from the campsite to the lake is 0.6 of the distance from the campsite to the hiking trails. The distance from the campsite to the hiking trails is 1.4 kilometers. What is the distance from the campsite to the lake?

4. Ryan brought 6 bags of marshmallows to roast over a campfire. Each bag weighs 0.625 pound. How many pounds do the bags of marshmallows weigh in all?

5. Rick and his family spent 1.25 hours setting up their tent. They spent 1.04 as much time unpacking their camping supplies. How much time did Rick and his family spend unpacking their camping supplies?

6. A family packed 2.04 pounds of dried fruit for their camping trip. They ate the same amount of dried fruit on each of 3 days. How much dried fruit did they eat each day?

7. Ellen cooked veggie burgers over a campfire. She used 2.8 pounds of veggie mix to make the burgers. Each burger weighed 0.35 pound. How many veggie burgers did Ellen cook?

8. Campers hiked 8.82 miles in 4.2 hours. If they walked at the same speed for the entire hike, how many miles did they hike each hour?

9. Nick bought new lanterns for a camping trip. He spent a total of $37.45. Each lantern cost $7.49. How many lanterns did Nick buy?

10. Two families went on a canoe trip. They traveled 34.83 miles in 5.4 hours. If they paddled at the same speed for the entire canoe trip, how many miles did they travel each hour?

LEARN

Explore Rational Numbers (A)

Number Lines and Opposite Integers

Use the number line to solve the problems.

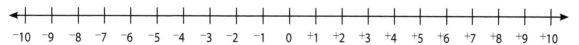

1. What is the opposite of ⁻6?

2. What is the opposite of ⁺4?

3. What is |⁻7|?

4. What is |⁺2|?

5. Is ⁻6 greater than or less than ⁺2?

6. Is ⁻5 greater than or less than ⁻3?

Name the integer that has a dot on it on the number line.

7.

8.

9.

10.

Choose the answer.

11. Which number line shows a dot on ⁻4?

A.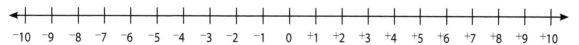

B.

C.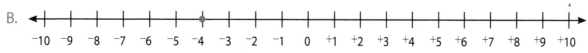

D.

T R Y   I T

12. Which number line shows a dot on ⁻7?

A.
-10 -9 -8 -7 -6 -5 -4 -3 -2 -1 0 +1 +2 +3 +4 +5 +6 +7 +8 +9 +10

B.
-10 -9 -8 -7 -6 -5 -4 -3 -2 -1 0 +1 +2 +3 +4 +5 +6 +7 +8 +9 +10

C.
-10 -9 -8 -7 -6 -5 -4 -3 -2 -1 0 +1 +2 +3 +4 +5 +6 +7 +8 +9 +10

D.
-10 -9 -8 -7 -6 -5 -4 -3 -2 -1 0 +1 +2 +3 +4 +5 +6 +7 +8 +9 +10

13. Which number line shows a dot on ⁺4?

A.
-10 -9 -8 -7 -6 -5 -4 -3 -2 -1 0 +1 +2 +3 +4 +5 +6 +7 +8 +9 +10

B.
-10 -9 -8 -7 -6 -5 -4 -3 -2 -1 0 +1 +2 +3 +4 +5 +6 +7 +8 +9 +10

C.
-10 -9 -8 -7 -6 -5 -4 -3 -2 -1 0 +1 +2 +3 +4 +5 +6 +7 +8 +9 +10

D.
-10 -9 -8 -7 -6 -5 -4 -3 -2 -1 0 +1 +2 +3 +4 +5 +6 +7 +8 +9 +10

14. Which integer has a dot on it on this number line?

-10 -9 -8 -7 -6 -5 -4 -3 -2 -1 0 +1 +2 +3 +4 +5 +6 +7 +8 +9 +10

A. ⁻1   B. 0   C. ⁺1   D. ⁺10

Challenge Question

Use the number line below. Write the integers in order from least to greatest.

-10 -9 -8 -7 -6 -5 -4 -3 -2 -1 0 +1 +2 +3 +4 +5 +6 +7 +8 +9 +10

15. ⁻4, ⁻7, ⁺6, ⁻1, ⁺5, 0, ⁺2, ⁻3

T R Y   I T

Explore Rational Numbers (B)

Fractions and Decimals on a Number Line

Use the number line to solve Problems 1–4.

1. What is the opposite of $-\frac{1}{3}$?

2. What is the opposite of $+1\frac{2}{3}$?

3. What is the opposite of $-1\frac{1}{3}$?

4. What is the opposite of $+\frac{2}{3}$?

Use the number line to solve Problems 5–8.

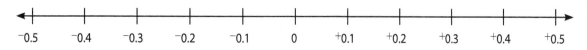

5. What is the opposite of -0.2?

6. What is the opposite of $+0.5$?

7. What is the opposite of $+0.1$?

8. What is the opposite of -0.3?

Read the problem and follow the directions.

9. Name the decimal number that is shown with a dot on this number line.

10. Name the mixed number that is shown with a dot on this number line.
    Express your answer in simplest form.

11. Name the numbers that are shown with dots on this number line.

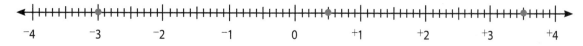

T R Y   I T

12. Name the numbers that are shown with dots on this number line.

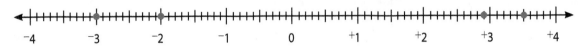

Choose the answer.

13. Which numbers are shown with dots on this number line?

A. $^-1.5, ^+1.5, ^+4\frac{1}{5}, ^+4.5$

B. $^-1.5, ^+1.5, ^+4\frac{1}{5}, ^+5.3$

C. $^-1.5, ^+1.5, ^+4\frac{1}{5}, ^+5.5$

D. $^-1.5, ^+1.5, ^+4\frac{2}{5}, ^+5.5$

14. Which numbers are shown with dots on this number line?

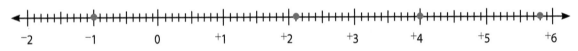

A. $^-1, ^+2\frac{1}{10}, ^+5.8, ^+6$

B. $^-1, ^+2\frac{1}{10}, ^+4, ^+4.8$

C. $^-1, ^+2\frac{2}{10}, ^+4, ^+5.8$

D. $^-1, ^+2\frac{1}{10}, ^+4, ^+5.8$

Challenge Question

Use the number line to write a description.

15. Describe in a sentence the location of $^-0.375$.

TRY IT

Explore Rational Numbers (C)

Locate Numbers on a Number Line

Worked Examples

You can compare positive and negative numbers by using a number line.

PROBLEM Is $^-1$ greater than or less than $^-0.5$?

SOLUTION

$$-2\frac{1}{2} \quad -2\frac{1}{4} \quad ^-2 \quad -1\frac{3}{4} \quad -1\frac{1}{2} \quad -1\frac{1}{4} \quad ^-1 \quad -\frac{3}{4} \quad -\frac{1}{2} \quad -\frac{1}{4} \quad 0 \quad +\frac{1}{4} \quad +\frac{1}{2} \quad +\frac{3}{4} \quad ^+1 \quad +1\frac{1}{4} \quad +1\frac{1}{2} \quad +1\frac{3}{4} \quad ^+2 \quad +2\frac{1}{4} \quad +2\frac{1}{2}$$

$$-2.5 \quad ^-2.25 \quad ^-2 \quad ^-1.75 \quad ^-1.5 \quad ^-1.25 \quad ^-1 \quad ^-0.75 \quad ^-0.5 \quad ^-0.25 \quad 0 \quad ^+0.25 \quad ^+0.5 \quad ^+0.75 \quad ^+1 \quad ^+1.25 \quad ^+1.5 \quad ^+1.75 \quad ^+2 \quad ^+2.25 \quad ^+2.5$$

ANSWER $^-1$ is less than $^-0.5$ because it is to the left of $^-1$ on the number line.

Describe where each point is on the number line in the Worked Examples.

1. $^+1.5$

2. $^-1\frac{3}{4}$

3. $^+2$

4. $^-0.5$

Answer "greater than" or "less than."

5. Is $^-2$ greater than or less than $^+1$?

6. Is $^+\frac{3}{4}$ greater than or less than $^-\frac{3}{4}$

7. Is $^-1.5$ greater than or less than $^-1$?

8. Is $^+1$ greater than or less than $^-2\frac{1}{2}$?

9. Is $^-2$ greater than or less than $^+2.5$?

LEARN

Explore Rational Numbers (C)

Practice Locating Numbers

Make a number line from ⁻2.0 to ⁺2.0, showing fourths. Make tick marks, number them with either decimals or fractions, and mark them with dots to show the location of each number.

1. 0

2. ⁺0.25

3. ⁻1.0

4. $^{+}\frac{3}{4}$

5. $^{+}1\frac{1}{4}$

6. ⁻1.5

7. $^{-}\frac{1}{2}$

Read the problem and follow the directions.

8. Name the decimal number that is shown with a dot on this number line.

9. Name the mixed number that is shown with a dot on this number line. Express your answer in simplest form.

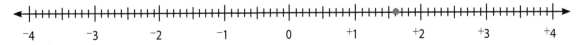

10. Name the integer that is shown with a dot on this number line.

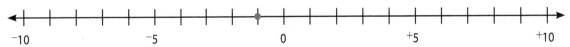

11. Name the dots that are shown on this number line.

12. Name the dots that are shown on this number line.

TRY IT

Choose the answer.

13. Which number line shows dots at ⁻2, ⁺2.2, and ⁺3½?

A.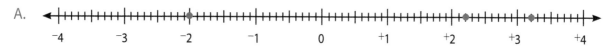

B.

C.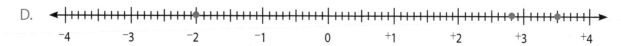

D.

14. Which numbers are shown with dots on this number line?

A. ⁻3.5, ⁺1½, ⁺2.5, ⁺3

B. ⁻3, ⁺1½, ⁺2.5, ⁺3

C. ⁻3, ⁺1½, ⁺2.5, ⁺3.5

D. ⁻3, ⁺1½, ⁺3, ⁺3.5

Challenge Question

Read the problem and follow the directions.

15. If someone forgot to place a negative sign in front of the tick mark on the number line for the number in Problem 6, how could you use your number line, the 1.5 with no sign on it, and the rest of the tick marks with numbers and signs to prove the number is negative?

T R Y   I T

Add and Subtract Integers (A)

Add Negatives and Subtract Positives

Worked Examples

You can add two negative integers.

PROBLEM 1 $^-12 + {}^-4 = ?$

SOLUTION

1 Start with 12 negative tiles.

2 Add 4 negative tiles.

3 End with 16 negative tiles.

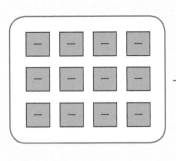

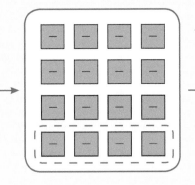

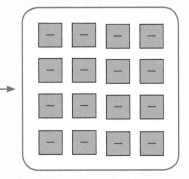

ANSWER $^-12 + {}^-4 = {}^-16$

Solve. Write the number sentence and the answer.

1. $^-7 + {}^-4 = \underline{?}$

2. A stock market is a place where stocks in companies are bought and sold. If people have stock in a company, then they own a part of the company. A daily stock market index tells people generally whether stocks sold at a higher or lower price compared with another time. On Monday, suppose the stock market index went down $^-5$ points. On Tuesday, suppose it went down $^-2$ more points. How many points did the index go down over the two days?

3. On another day, suppose the stock market index went down $^-12$ points in one hour and an additional $^-7$ points in the next hour. How many points did it go down in those two hours?

L E A R N

You can subtract a positive integer from a negative integer. When you subtract a positive integer from a negative integer, the problem is the same as adding a negative integer to a negative integer.

PROBLEM 2 $^{-}15 - {}^{+}4 = ?$

SOLUTION

1 Start with $^{-}15$.

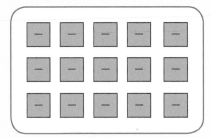

2 Add $^{-}4$ and $^{+}4$. You have added 0. By the zero property of addition, $^{-}15 + 0 = {}^{-}15$. The total value of the tiles has not changed.

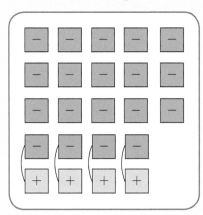

3 Subtract $^{+}4$.

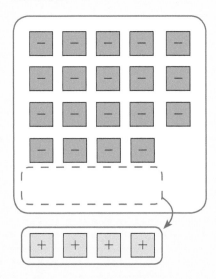

4 End with $^{-}19$.

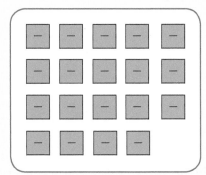

ANSWER $^{-}15 - {}^{+}4 = {}^{-}19$

LEARN

Solve. Write the number sentence and the answer.

4. $^-13 - {}^+4 = \underline{\ ?\ }$

5. $^-4 - {}^+9 = \underline{\ ?\ }$

6. You are playing a quiz game with your friends. You have answered a number of questions incorrectly. Your score is $^-8$ points. You answer the next question incorrectly and lose 4 more points. What is your new score?

Add and Subtract Integers (A)

Practice Adding and Subtracting

Add.

1. $^-10 + ^-6 = \underline{\;?\;}$

2. $^-12 + ^-15 = \underline{\;?\;}$

3. $^-8 + ^-6 = \underline{\;?\;}$

Subtract.

4. $^+23 - ^+18 = \underline{\;?\;}$

5. $^+67 - ^+28 = \underline{\;?\;}$

6. $^-2 - ^+8 = \underline{\;?\;}$

7. $^-12 - ^+13 = \underline{\;?\;}$

8. $^-54 - ^+43 = \underline{\;?\;}$

Choose the answer.

9. $^-6 + ^-2 = ?$

   A. $^+4$

   B. $^-4$

   C. $^-8$

   D. $^+8$

10. $^+5 + ^+3 = ?$

   A. $^+8$

   B. $^-8$

   C. $^-2$

   D. $^+2$

11. $^-43 - ^+10 = ?$

   A. $^-53$

   B. $^-33$

   C. $^+33$

   D. $^+53$

12. $^+83 - ^+9 = ?$

   A. $^-91$

   B. $^-74$

   C. $^+74$

   D. $^+91$

T R Y   I T

Add and Subtract Integers (B)

Temperature and Golf Story Problems

Worked Examples

You can add two negative integers.

PROBLEM 1 $^-5 + (^-13) = ?$

SOLUTION Add $^-5$ and $^-13$. Both numbers are negative, so the answer is negative. You can put parentheses around a number and its positive or negative sign when you compute with integers so it's clear that the sign goes with the number.

ANSWER $^-5 + ^-13 = ^-18$

Sometimes the numbers that are in everyday problems involve negative integers. You can use positive integers and negative integers to solve story problems about temperature.

PROBLEM 2 On January 12, the high temperature was $^-4°F$. The temperature dropped $6°F$ to reach the low temperature that day. What was the low temperature that day?

SOLUTION

1 $^-4 - ^+6 = ?$

2 When you subtract a positive integer from a negative integer, you are doing the same thing as if you were adding a negative integer to a negative integer.

$^-4 - ^+6 = ^-4 + ^-6$

$^-4 + ^-6 = ^-10$

ANSWER The low temperature on January 12 was $^-10°F$.

LOOK BACK You started with a negative integer. You subtracted a positive integer from it and the answer is a negative integer. Sometimes when you add and subtract integers, the answer will be a positive integer, and at other times, the answer will be a negative integer. It depends on the integers.

You can use positive integers and negative integers to solve story problems about golf.

Facts about golf: In golf, *par* means the number of strokes an expert golfer uses to hit the ball into a particular hole. Par is different for the different holes on a golf course. In a game, players often keep track of how many strokes under par or over par their score is. You can think of strokes under par as negative integers and strokes over par as positive integers. For example, par for nine holes might be 20 strokes. If a player uses 19 strokes while playing those nine holes, he has shot 1 under par.

PROBLEM 3 Miguel played 18 holes of golf on Saturday. For the first half of the game, he shot 2 under par. For the second half of the game, he shot 3 under par. What was Miguel's score at the end of his game?

SOLUTION Add the given integers. Because each one stands for a golf score that is under par, they are negative numbers.
$^-2 + {}^-3 = ?$

A negative integer plus a negative integer equals a negative integer.
$^-2 + {}^-3 = {}^-5$

ANSWER Miguel's score was 5 under par at the end of his game.

Solve. Use a number line to help you solve the problem, if needed.

1. $^-4 - {}^+6 = \underline{?}$

2. $^-7 - {}^+11 = \underline{?}$

Use this story problem for Problems 3–7. Sketch a number line to help you solve the problems, if needed.

In Central Park in New York City on New Year's Day, the high temperature was 26°F. The temperature dropped 11°F to get to the day's low temperature. What was the low temperature that day?

3. Is the high temperature above or below zero?

4. Is the amount the temperature dropped greater than or less than the high temperature of 26°F?

5. Will the low temperature be above or below zero? Why?

6. Write a number sentence using integers and an answer for the problem.

7. Go back to the original problem and write a sentence to answer the question.

111

LEARN

Read the problem and follow the directions.

8. The average daily high temperature in Birmingham, Alabama, in October is 74°F. In December, the average daily high temperature is 19°F below the daily high temperature in October.

   What is the average daily high temperature in December?

Use this story problem for Problems 9–13. Sketch a number line to help you solve the problems, if needed.

Susan played 18 holes of golf on Saturday. She shot 3 under par for the first half of her game. She shot 1 under par for the second half of her game. What was Susan's score at the end of her game?

9. Was her first score above or below zero?

10. Was her second score above or below zero?

11. Will her score at the end of the game be above or below zero?

12. Write a number sentence using integers and an answer for the problem.

13. Go back to the original problem and write a sentence to answer the question.

LEARN

Add and Subtract Integers (B)

Practice with Integers

Write a number sentence and solve the problem. Then write the answer to the problem.

1. The morning temperature was $^-6°F$. The temperature decreased 15 degrees throughout the day. What was the temperature at the end of the day?

Add.

2. $^-19 + {}^-13 = $ _?_

3. $^+9 + {}^+1 = $ _?_

4. Yolanda had a golf score of $^-5$ after the first three holes. She got $^-3$ on the next hole. What is Yolanda's score now?

5. The men's golf team had a score of $^-10$ after the first three holes. They got $^-4$ on the next hole. What was the golf team's score after four holes?

Subtract.

6. $^+60 - {}^+32 = $ _?_

7. $^-9 - ({}^+19) = $ _?_

8. The temperature was $^-6°C$ at noon. The temperature dropped 2°C by sunset. What was the temperature at sunset?

9. The temperature was $^-4°C$ at noon. The temperature dropped 9°C by midnight. What was the temperature at midnight?

Choose the answer.

10. The temperature at 6 a.m. was $^-7°C$. The temperature dropped 8°C by 4 p.m. What was the temperature at 4 p.m.?

   A. $^+15°C$ B. $^-15°C$ C. $^+1°C$ D. $^-1°C$

T R Y   I T

Add and Subtract Integers (C)

Write and Solve Ocean Story Problems

Some ocean animals live above sea level, others at sea level, and others below sea level. Use positive and negative integers to write addition and subtraction story problems about these ocean animals.

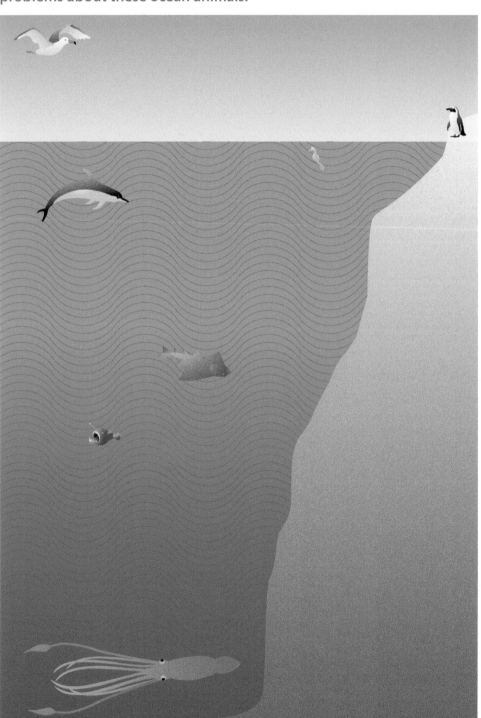

Salvin's albatross
30 meters above

African penguin
sea level or 0 meters

big-belly seahorse
5 meters below

Atlantic spotted dolphin
12 meters below

angel shark
150 meters below

anglerfish
200 meters below

giant squid
550 meters below

114

Integer Answers: Reasonable or Not?

General Statements About Integer Math

You can make general statements about the kinds of answers you will get when you add and subtract positive and negative integers in certain ways. You can use the general statements to verify the reasonableness of answers.

PROBLEM 1 $^+8 - {}^+5 = ?$

SOLUTION When you subtract a positive integer from a greater positive integer, the difference will always be a positive integer less than the first number in the number sentence. The difference is 0 if the minuend and subtrahend are the same number.

It is reasonable that the answer will be a positive integer less than the first number in the number sentence.

ANSWER $^+8 - {}^+5 = {}^+3$

PROBLEM 2 $^+4 + {}^+5 = ?$

SOLUTION When you add two positive integers, the sum will be a positive integer greater than either of the two addends.

It is reasonable that the answer will be a positive integer greater than either of the two addends.

ANSWER $^+4 + {}^+5 = {}^+9$

PROBLEM 3 $^-2 + {}^-6 = ?$

SOLUTION When you add two negative integers, the sum is a negative integer less than either of the two addends.

It is reasonable that the answer will be a negative integer less than either of the two addends.

ANSWER $^-2 + {}^-6 = {}^-8$

L E A R N

PROBLEM 4 $^-5 - {}^+2 = ?$

SOLUTION When you subtract a positive integer from a negative integer, the difference is a negative integer less than either of the other numbers in the number sentence.

It is reasonable that the answer will be a negative integer that is less than either of the other numbers in the number sentence.

ANSWER $^-5 - {}^+2 = {}^-7$

Solve each number sentence. Then decide if your answer is reasonable.

1. $^-6 + {}^-9 = \underline{\ ?\ }$

2. $^+19 + {}^+13 = \underline{\ ?\ }$

3. $^+14 - {}^+5 = \underline{\ ?\ }$

4. $^-11 - ({}^+4) = \underline{\ ?\ }$

5. $^-50 + {}^-33 = \underline{\ ?\ }$

6. $^+32 + {}^+21 = \underline{\ ?\ }$

7. $^+29 - {}^+15 = \underline{\ ?\ }$

8. $^-25 - ({}^+10) = \underline{\ ?\ }$

LEARN

Integer Answers: Reasonable or Not?

Verify Reasonableness

Worked Examples

You can verify that the answer to an integer addition or subtraction problem is reasonable by applying general statements that are true about adding and subtracting positive and negative integers.

- When you subtract a positive integer from a greater positive integer, the difference will always be a positive integer less than the first number in the number sentence. The difference is 0 if the minuend and subtrahend are the same number.
- When you add two positive integers, the sum will be a positive integer greater than either of the two addends.
- When you add two negative integers, the sum is a negative integer less than either of the two addends.
- When you subtract a positive integer from a negative integer, the difference is a negative integer less than either of the other numbers in the number sentence.

PROBLEM 1 Martin said that $^-43 + {}^-47$ equals $^-90$. Is Martin's answer reasonable?

SOLUTION The problem asks you to add two negative integers and decide if the sum, a negative integer, is reasonable. When you add two negative integers, the sum is a negative integer less than either of the two addends.

If you think about starting at $^-43$ on the number line and moving 47 spaces to the left (to add $^-47$), you will get $^-90$.

ANSWER Yes, Martin's answer is reasonable. He correctly found that $^-43 + {}^-47 = {}^-90$. He correctly answered that the sum of two negative integers is a negative integer that is less than either of the two addends.

PROBLEM 2 Sierra solved this problem: Elian's score in a quiz game was $^+52$ points. Elian answered his next question correctly and got $^+13$ points. How many points does Elian have now? Sierra thought the answer was $^-65$ points. Is Sierra's answer reasonable?

SOLUTION The problem asks you to add two positive integers and decide if the given sum, a negative integer, is reasonable. When you add two positive integers, the sum will be a positive integer greater than either of the two addends.

If you think about starting with 52 positive tiles and adding 13 positive tiles, you get a total of 65 positive tiles.

L E A R N

ANSWER No, Sierra's answer is not reasonable. She found an incorrect answer to the problem. $^+52 + {}^+13 = {}^+65$, not $^-65$. Her answer should have shown that the sum of two positive integers is a positive integer that is greater than either of the two addends. Elian has $^+65$ points.

PROBLEM 3 Jabar solved this problem: The temperature was $^-4°C$ at midnight. The temperature dropped 3°C by 5 a.m. What was the temperature at 5 a.m.? Jabar thought the answer was $^-1°C$. Is Jabar's answer reasonable?

SOLUTION The problem asks you to subtract a positive integer from a negative integer and decide if the given difference, a negative integer greater than the first number in the subtraction problem, is reasonable. When you subtract a positive integer from a negative integer, the difference is a negative integer less than either of the other numbers in the number sentence.

If you think about making an arrow to show $^-4$ on a number line and adding an arrow that shows $^+3$, the sketched arrows will show the difference is $^-7$.

ANSWER No, Jabar's answer is not reasonable. He found an incorrect answer to the problem. $^-4 - {}^+3 = {}^-7$, not $^-1$. His answer should have shown that when you subtract a positive integer from a negative integer, the difference is a negative integer less than either of the other numbers in the number sentence. The temperature at 5 a.m. was $^-7°C$.

Decide if the answer given by the problem solver is reasonable. Explain why or why not.

1. Travis solved this problem: A professional golfer had a golf score of $^-12$ after three games. She got a score of $^-5$ on the fourth day. What is the golfer's score after four days? Travis thought the answer was $^+7$. Is Travis's answer reasonable? Explain.

2. Debra solved this problem: The temperature at daybreak was $^+56°F$. By sunset, the temperature had risen $^+14°F$. Debra said the temperature at sunset was $^+70°F$. Is Debra's answer reasonable? Explain.

3. Andrew solved this problem: Kai got a score of $^+24$ points the first time he played a game. He scored $^+11$ points the second time he played the game. What is the difference between the two scores? Andrew thought the answer was $^+13$ points. Is Andrew's answer reasonable? Explain.

4. Don says that $^-21 - (^+8)$ equals $^+13$. Is Don's answer reasonable?

LEARN

Unit Review

Checkpoint Practice

Read the problem and follow the directions.

1. Name the decimal number that is shown with a dot on this number line.

2. Name the mixed number that is shown with a dot on this number line. Express your answer in simplest form.

Choose the answer.

3. Which number line shows a dot on $^+2.6$?

A.

B.

C.

D.

4. Which decimal number is shown with a dot on this number line?

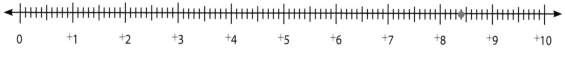

A. $^+4.0$ B. $^+8.0$ C. $^+8.4$ D. $^+8.6$

5. Which mixed number is shown with a dot on this number line?

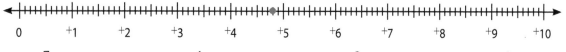

A. $^+4\frac{7}{10}$ B. $^+4\frac{4}{5}$ C. $^+5\frac{2}{10}$ D. $^+5\frac{1}{5}$

UNIT REVIEW

6. Which integer is shown with a dot on this number line?

A. $^+2$ B. $^-2$ C. $^-8$ D. $^+8$

7. Which number line shows a dot on $^-3$?

A.

B.

C.

D.

8. Which number line shows a dot on $^-2$, $^+0.5$, and $^+1\frac{1}{2}$?

A.

B.

C.

D.

9. Which numbers are shown with dots on this number line?

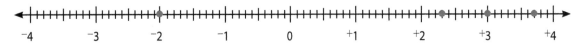

A. $^-2, ^+3, ^+3.2, ^+3\frac{7}{10}$ B. $^-3, ^+2, ^+2.3, ^+3\frac{7}{10}$

C. $^-2, ^+2.3, ^+3, ^+3\frac{7}{10}$ D. $^-2, ^+2.3, ^+3, ^+3\frac{6}{10}$

Understand Percents (B)

Find Percents in Story Problems

> ### Worked Examples
>
> You can find a percent when you know how many things out of 100 there are. When you already know the percent, you can find the number of things out of 100.
>
> - In a survey, a library asked 100 children what type of book they liked the most. The choices were mysteries, historical fiction, science fiction, fantasies, nonfiction, and realistic fiction. The survey results showed that 51 out of the 100 children liked realistic fiction the most. It also showed that 33% of the children liked mysteries the most.
>
> **PROBLEM 1** What percent of the children liked realistic fiction the most?
>
> **SOLUTION** Percent means "out of 100" or "of each 100." The problem says that 51 out of the 100 children liked realistic fiction the most. To find the percent, think about 51 out of 100, or $\frac{51}{100}$. That fraction is the same as 51%.
>
> **ANSWER** In the survey, 51% of the children liked realistic fiction the most.
>
> ---
>
> **PROBLEM 2** How many children liked mysteries the most?
>
> **SOLUTION** The problem says that 33% liked mysteries the most. That means that 33 out of the 100 children liked mysteries the most.
>
> **ANSWER** In the survey, 33 children answered that they liked mysteries the most.

L E A R N

Solve.

1. One day, a movie rental store had 100 customers who rented one movie each. Of the 100 movies rented, 85 were rented after 5:00 p.m. What percent of the movies were rented after 5:00 p.m.?

2. Sally had 64 cents. What percent of one dollar is 64 cents?

3. Tommy collects toy monkeys. He has 100 different toy monkeys. In Tommy's collection, 45% of his toy monkeys are stuffed animals. How many of his toy monkeys are stuffed animals?

4. Kathy buys 100 stickers. She finds that 20 of the stickers have cats on them. What percent of Kathy's stickers have cats on them?

5. A restaurant includes a toy dog, cat, or fish with every children's meal sold. For every 100 meals sold, 34 of them include a toy dog. What percent of meals include a toy dog?

6. The Tigers baseball team gave away hats to the first 100 fans at the ballpark last Saturday. After the game, 67% of the fans were still wearing their hats. How many of the first 100 fans were still wearing their hats?

Find Equivalents to Percents (A)
Fraction and Decimal Story Problems

Worked Examples

You can write a decimal number that is equivalent to a fraction. A fraction can be equivalent to more than one decimal number.

PROBLEM Jacob ate $\frac{1}{2}$ of his lima beans. Write two decimal numbers to express how much of his lima beans he ate.

SOLUTION

1 To express $\frac{1}{2}$ as a decimal number in tenths, first find an equivalent fraction with a denominator of 10.

$$\frac{1}{2} = \frac{?}{10}$$

2 Multiply the numerator and denominator by the same value. The denominator was multiplied by 5 to get 10, so multiply the numerator by 5.

$$\frac{1}{2} = \frac{5}{10}$$

3 Find one decimal equivalent of $\frac{5}{10}$, which is 0.5.

$$\frac{1}{2} = \frac{5}{10} = 0.5$$

4 To express $\frac{1}{2}$ as a decimal number in hundredths, find an equivalent fraction with a denominator of 100.

$$\frac{1}{2} = \frac{?}{100}$$

5 Multiply the numerator and denominator by the same value. The denominator was multiplied by 50 to get 100, so multiply the numerator by 50.

$$\frac{1}{2} = \frac{50}{100}$$

6 Find another decimal equivalent of $\frac{5}{10}$, which is 0.50.

$$\frac{1}{2} = \frac{50}{100} = 0.50$$

ANSWER Jacob ate 0.5, or 0.50, of his lima beans.

L E A R N

Solve. Show the answer as equivalent fractions and decimal numbers with equals symbols between them.

1. Sarah ran $\frac{3}{4}$ of a mile. Express the amount she ran as a decimal number.

2. Of the players on Billy's team, $\frac{4}{10}$ liked the orange sports drink the best. Express the amount as a decimal number.

3. Bill ordered a quarter-pound hamburger. What is the equivalent decimal for that amount?

4. Kelsey's family ate $\frac{4}{5}$ of a pizza. Express the amount Kelsey's family ate as a decimal number.

Worked Examples

You can write a decimal number that is equivalent to a fraction with 1,000 as the denominator.

PROBLEM A team of scientists wanted to know how many corn kernels were on each of 1,000 ears of corn that had not received enough rain. The scientists counted the corn kernels on 391 ears of corn on the first day of their research study. What decimal number expresses how many ears of corn they checked?

SOLUTION

1 Write a fraction to express the number of ears of corn they checked out of the total number of ears of corn.

$\frac{391}{1,000}$

2 Since the fraction is already written as a fraction with a denominator of 1,000, write the decimal equivalent without first finding an equivalent fraction.

$\frac{391}{1,000} = 0.391$

ANSWER The team of scientists checked 0.391 of the total ears of corn.

Solve. Show the answer as equivalent fractions and decimal numbers with equals symbols between them.

5. Justine is running a 1,000-meter race. By noon, she had completed $\frac{762}{1,000}$ of the race. What portion of the race has she completed so far? Express the amount as a decimal number.

6. At the Lap Around Race, cars have completed $\frac{276}{1,000}$ of the race. What portion of the race has been completed so far? Express the amount as a decimal number.

7. A survey of 1,000 people asked how many of them woke up without using an alarm clock. The results were that 198 of the people surveyed woke up without using an alarm clock. Express the amount as a decimal number.

LEARN

Find Equivalents to Percents (B)

Fraction and Percent Story Problems

Worked Examples

You can write a percent that is equivalent to a fraction.

PROBLEM 1 While Mark was mowing the lawn, it got dark outside. He finished $\frac{1}{2}$ of the lawn before he had to stop. What percent of the lawn did he finish mowing?

SOLUTION

1 To write $\frac{1}{2}$ as a percent, begin by writing the fraction, then an equals sign, and then a fraction with a denominator of 100 and a missing numerator.

$$\frac{1}{2} = \frac{?}{100}$$

2 To create an equivalent fraction, multiply the numerator and denominator by the same value. The 2 was multiplied by 50 to get the equivalent denominator of 100. To find the equivalent numerator, multiply 1 by the same number, 50.

$$\frac{1}{2} = \frac{50}{100}$$

$\frac{50}{100}$ can be written as 50%.

$$\frac{1}{2} = \frac{50}{100} = 50\%$$

ANSWER Mark finished mowing 50% of his lawn before it got dark outside.

You can write a fraction with a denominator of 100 that is equivalent to a percent.

PROBLEM 2 Felice read 38% of her new book on Sunday. How much of the book did Felice read, written as an equivalent fraction with a denominator of 100?

SOLUTION To write 38% as a fraction with a denominator of 100, begin by writing the percent and then an equals sign. Change the percent to a fraction with a denominator of 100.

$$38\% = \frac{38}{100}$$

38% can be written as $\frac{38}{100}$.

ANSWER Felice read $\frac{38}{100}$ of her new book.

L E A R N

Solve. Show the answers as equivalent fractions and percents with equals symbols between them.

1. Larry exercises every day. Each day, $\frac{3}{5}$ of his exercise time is spent jogging. What percent of his exercise time is spent jogging?

2. Hanna made pizza for dinner. She put pineapple on $\frac{1}{4}$ of the pizza. What percent of the pizza had pineapple?

3. Corey ran $\frac{45}{100}$ of the race and walked the rest. What percent of the race did he run?

4. Carrie read $\frac{9}{10}$ of her book. What percent of her book did Carrie read?

5. For a special treat, Reese made a cake for her family. They ate $\frac{4}{5}$ of the cake. What percent of the cake did her family eat?

6. Some of the animals in an animal preserve live on land and some live in the water. At the preserve, 82 out of 100 animals, or $\frac{82}{100}$, live on land. What percent of the animals in the preserve live on land?

Solve. Show the answers as equivalent percents and fractions with equals symbols between them.

7. Katie's music group is preparing for a concert. At that performance, 55% of the performers will play solos. How many performers will play solos, written as an equivalent fraction with a denominator of 100?

8. Amador visited 17% of his customers during the week. How many customers did Amador visit, written as an equivalent fraction with a denominator of 100?

LEARN

Find Equivalents to Percents (B)

Practice Finding Equivalent Percents

Write a percent equivalent to the fraction.

1. $\frac{34}{50}$

2. $\frac{2}{5}$

3. $\frac{42}{100}$

4. $\frac{90}{100}$

5. $\frac{1}{25}$

6. $\frac{8}{100}$

Write a fraction equivalent to the percent. Make the fraction have a denominator of 100.

7. 58%

8. 19%

9. 3%

10. 39%

Solve.

11. Susan ate $\frac{1}{5}$ of her sandwich. What percent of her sandwich did she eat?

12. Timmy read $\frac{4}{10}$ of the book. What percent of the book did he read?

13. Ryan made a snack mix. In his mix, $\frac{3}{4}$ of the ingredients are nuts. What percent of the snack mix is nuts?

14. Steven shaded $\frac{13}{25}$ of a grid. What percent of the grid did he shade?

Answer using complete sentences.

15. Explain how to change $\frac{2}{5}$ to a percent.

TRY IT

Find Equivalents to Percents (C)

Story Problems with Equivalents

Worked Examples

When a story problem asks for a fraction, decimal number, or percent, you can find the answer by using the information in the problem to write an equivalent fraction, decimal number, or percent.

PROBLEM 1 Pat has 50 shirts to wash. He has washed 20 shirts. What percent of the shirts has he washed?

SOLUTION

1 To write a percent for the number of shirts that Pat has washed, first think about the problem. So far, he has washed 20 out of 50 shirts, so the fraction of shirts he has washed is $\frac{20}{50}$.

2 To find the equivalent percent, first write an equivalent fraction for $\frac{20}{50}$ with a denominator of 100 and a missing numerator.

$$\frac{20}{50} = \frac{?}{100}$$

3 Multiply the numerator and denominator by the same value to find an equivalent fraction. The denominator was multiplied by 2 to get 100, so multiply the numerator by 2.

$$\frac{20}{50} = \frac{40}{100}$$

4 Find the equivalent percent for $\frac{40}{100}$, which is 40%.

ANSWER Pat has washed 40% of the shirts.

PROBLEM 2 A pizza has 25 pieces of green pepper on it. Charles ate 48% of the pieces of green pepper. What decimal number shows the amount of green pepper he ate?

SOLUTION

1 To write a decimal number for the amount of green pepper Charles ate, first think about the problem. The problem says that Charles ate 48% of the pieces, so the fraction of the green pepper he ate is $\frac{48}{100}$.

2 Find the equivalent decimal number for $\frac{48}{100}$, which is 0.48.

ANSWER Charles ate 0.48 of the green pepper.

PROBLEM 3 Antoine went to an aquarium where there were 400 different species of animals. He saw 124 of the animal species. What decimal number represents the number of animal species Antoine saw?

SOLUTION

1 To write a decimal number for the number of species of animals he saw, first think about the problem. The problem says that Antoine saw 124 of 400 species of animals, so the fraction to represent the information in the problem is $\frac{124}{400}$.

2 Write an equivalent fraction with a denominator of 100 and a missing numerator.

$$\frac{124}{400} = \frac{?}{100}$$

3 The fraction has a denominator greater than 100, so divide, rather than multiply, to get an equivalent fraction with a denominator of 100. Divide the numerator and denominator by the same value to find an equivalent fraction. The denominator, 400, was divided by 4 to get 100. Divide the numerator, 124, by 4 to get 31.

$$\frac{124}{400} = \frac{31}{100}$$

4 Find the decimal number for $\frac{31}{100}$, which is 0.31.

ANSWER Antoine saw 0.31 of the animal species at the aquarium.

Solve. Show the answer as equivalent fractions, decimal numbers, or percents, depending on the problem, with the equals symbols between them.

1. Tom ordered 400 snacks for camp. In his order, 120 of the snacks were cheese crackers. What percent of the snacks were cheese crackers?

2. Stacy ran $\frac{9}{20}$ of the race and walked the rest. What decimal number shows how much of the race she ran?

3. There are 300 pages in the book Gina is reading. She has read through page 60. What percent of the book has she read?

4. On a horse ranch, 39% of the horses are pintos. The horse ranch has 200 horses. How many horses are pintos?

5. In the children's section of the bookstore, $\frac{82}{200}$ of the books are picture books. What percent of the children's books are picture books?

6. On a sports survey, $\frac{34}{100}$ people said they liked baseball more than basketball. What decimal number shows how many people liked baseball more than basketball?

7. A boat has traveled 78 miles of a 300-mile river. What decimal number shows the number of miles that the boat has traveled along the river?

8. A path was 700 feet long. Darien walked 560 feet down the path. What percent of the path did he walk?

LEARN

Percent of a Number (A)

Percent of 100

Worked Examples

You can find how many out of 100 if you know the percent. You can find the percent if you know how many out of 100.

PROBLEM 1 The owner of a hat company wanted to know what percent of people wear hats at baseball games. He decided to collect data at an afternoon game. He kept track of how many of the first 100 people who arrived at the ballpark wore hats. He wrote the data as a percent. On that day, 79% of the first 100 people who arrived wore hats. How many people wore hats?

SOLUTION

1 Finding 79% of 100 is the same as multiplying 79% by 100. Write 79% as a fraction and a decimal number.

$$79\% = \frac{79}{100} = 0.79$$

2 Multiply the decimal number by 100.

$$0.79 \times 100 = 79$$

ANSWER Of the first 100 people who arrived at the baseball game, the number who wore hats was 79.

PROBLEM 2 The owner of a hat company wanted to know what percent of people wear hats to hockey games. She decided to collect data at a Saturday night game. She counted how many of the first 100 people who arrived for a hockey game wore hats. On that night, 27 of the first 100 people who arrived wore hats. What percent of the first 100 people wore hats?

SOLUTION

1 Write 27 of 100 as a fraction.

$$\frac{27}{100}$$

2 Change the fraction to an equivalent decimal number and then to an equivalent percent.

$$\frac{27}{100} = 0.27 = 27\%$$

ANSWER Of the first 100 people who arrived at the hockey game, 27% wore hats.

L E A R N

Solve.

1. A survey of 100 dog owners found that 89% of the owners walked their dog that day. How many of the dog owners walked their dog that day?

2. The book club made a list of books to read and discuss at upcoming meetings and asked the members to vote on what type of book to read. Of the 100 people who voted, 42 people wanted to read a biography. What percent of the 100 people wanted to read a biography?

3. What is 62% of 100?

4. What is 7% of 100?

5. 29 is what percent of 100?

6. What is 9% of 100?

7. What is 65% of 100?

8. 70 is what percent of 100?

9. 50 is what percent of 100?

LEARN

Percent of a Number (A)

Practice Finding Percents

Solve.

1. At the Run to the Trees marathon, 4 out of 100 runners finished before noon. What percent of the runners finished before noon?

2. To qualify for the county spelling bee, each contestant had to spell 100 words. Kate spelled 98% of the 100 words correctly. How many words did Kate spell correctly?

3. What is 34% of 100?

4. What is 2% of 100?

5. What is 7% of 100?

6. What is 18% of 100?

7. 12 is what percent of 100?

8. 32 is what percent of 100?

9. 8 is what percent of 100?

10. 71 is what percent of 100?

11. 60 is what percent of 100?

12. 83 is what percent of 100?

Choose the answer.

13. What is 75% of 100?

    A. 750   B. 75   C. 7.5   D. 0.75

TRY IT

Percent of a Number (B)

Different Ways to Find Percent

Worked Examples

You can use different methods to find percents of numbers less than 100 and greater than 100.

PROBLEM 1 What is 20% of 60?

SOLUTION 1 $0.20 \times 60 = ?$
$0.20 \times 60 = 12$

SOLUTION 2

1. Shortcut: Start by multiplying 10% by 60. 10% is equivalent to 0.10.

   $0.10 \times 60 = 6$

2. Remember that the original problem asked for 20% of 60, and you just found 10% of 60. To find 20% of a number, find 10% of the number and multiply the answer by 2, because 20% is twice as much as 10%.

   $6 \times 2 = 12$

ANSWER 20% of 60 is 12.

PROBLEM 2 What is 50% of 80?

SOLUTION 1 $0.50 \times 80 = ?$
$0.50 \times 80 = 40$

SOLUTION 2

1. Shortcut: Think of 50% as $\frac{50}{100}$, which is $\frac{1}{2}$. Another way to think of $\frac{1}{2}$ is that it is the same as half.

2. Find that half of 80 is 40.

ANSWER 50% of 80 is 40.

PROBLEM 3 What is 25% of 200?

SOLUTION

1. Shortcut: Since the factor 200 has zeros in the ones and tens places, place 2 zeros in the answer and then multiply by 2, the first nonzero digit in that factor. Finish by placing the decimal point.

2.
$$
\begin{array}{r}
0.25 \\
\times\ 2\,00 \\
\hline
50.00
\end{array}
$$

ANSWER 25% of 200 is 50.

L E A R N

PROBLEM 4 What is 10% of 95?

SOLUTION

1 $0.10 \times 95 = ?$
$0.10 \times 95 = 9.5$

2 Shortcut: Multiply the fraction for 0.10 by 95.

$$\frac{\cdot 1}{10} \times 95 = \frac{95}{10} = 9.5$$

ANSWER 10% of 95 is 9.5.

PROBLEM 5 Of the 450 people at the lake one day, 22% were fishing. How many people were fishing?

SOLUTION

1 Shortcut: Multiply the fraction for 22% by 450.

$$\frac{22}{100} \times 450 = \frac{9,900}{100} = 99$$

2 Multiply 450 by 0.22, the decimal number for 22%.

$$\begin{array}{r} \overset{1}{\cancel{4}}50 \\ \times\ 0.22 \\ \hline 900 \\ +\ 9,000 \\ \hline 99.00 \end{array}$$

ANSWER 22% of 450 is 99, so 99 people were fishing at the lake.

Use the methods from the Worked Examples to solve.

1. What is 10% of 55?

2. What is 20% of 55?

3. What is 30% of 55?

4. What is 50% of 350?

5. What is 20% of 72?

6. What is 10% of 72?

7. What is 30% of 400?

8. What is 10% of 202?

9. What is 20% of 202?

10. What is 30% of 202?

11. There are 350 campsites by the river. One day, the ranger reported that 14% of the campsites were vacant. How many campsites were vacant?

Percent of a Number (B)

Find Percents of Numbers

Solve.

1. What is 60% of 40?

2. What is 61% of 200?

3. What is 34% of 50?

4. What is 82% of 500?

5. What is 30% of 810?

6. What is 25% of 400?

7. Mike received 20 e-mails. He replied to 45% of them. How many e-mails did Mike reply to?

8. Phil was sending invitations to a party. He was inviting 40 people and had sent 75% of the invitations. How many invitations had Phil sent?

9. There were 90 employees at a bank and 10% rode their bikes to work. How many employees rode their bikes to work?

10. There were 68 children at the ice rink. At 7 p.m., 50% of them went home. How many children went home?

11. Ralph's cafe has 140 seats. At lunchtime, 20% of the seats were filled. How many seats were filled?

12. What is 10% of 32? What is 20% of 32? What is 30% of 32? Explain how you found the answers.

TRY IT

Percent of a Number (C)

Calculate Tips

Worked Examples

You can find a percent of a number to calculate the amount of a tip.

Facts about tips: A tip is money paid to workers to show satisfaction for their service. Another word for tip is *gratuity*. Tips are paid to people who provide services such as cutting hair or serving meals. A tip is usually a percent of the cost of the service. Many people consider 15% of the cost of the service a reasonable tip, although tips can be less than or greater than 15%. Whatever percent is used, the tip is calculated based on the cost of the service. The cost of the service and the tip are added together to find the total cost.

PROBLEM 1 Dan and his uncle have breakfast at a diner. The cost for breakfast is $12. They want to leave a 15% tip. How much money should the tip be?

SOLUTION 1 Finding a tip is just like finding the percent of a number. Write 15% as a decimal number and multiply by $12. ⟶ $0.15 \times 12 = 1.80$

SOLUTION 2

1. Break 15% into 10% and 5% because 10% + 5% equals 15%.
2. Find 10% of $12. ⟶ $0.10 \times 12 = 1.20$
3. Find 5% of $12. ⟶ $0.05 \times 12 = 0.60$
4. Add the two amounts. ⟶ $1.20 + 0.60 = 1.80$

SOLUTION 3

1. Break 15% into 10% and 5% because 10% + 5% equals 15%.
2. Find 10% of $12. ⟶ $0.10 \times 12 = 1.20$
3. Find half of the 10% tip. ⟶ $1.20 \div 2 = 0.60$
4. Add the two amounts to find the tip. ⟶ $1.20 + 0.60 = 1.80$

ANSWER A 15% tip on a $12 breakfast is $1.80.

LEARN

PROBLEM 2 The cost for a pizza is $17. If the pizza delivery person receives a 20% tip, how much tip will he receive?

SOLUTION 1 Write 20% as a decimal number and multiply by 17. $\longrightarrow$ $0.20 \times 17 = 3.40$

SOLUTION 2

1 Break 20% into 10% plus 10%, because 10% + 10% equals 20%.

2 Find 10% of $17. $\longrightarrow$ $0.10 \times 17 = 1.70$

3 Multiply $1.70 by 2 or add $1.70 + $1.70 to find twice the amount of a 10% tip.
- $1.70 \times 2 = 3.40$
- $1.70 + 1.70 = 3.40$

ANSWER The pizza delivery person will receive a $3.40 tip.

Solve.

1. The cost of a haircut is $30. Mrs. Sanchez wants to give a 15% tip. How much money should the tip be?

2. The bill for lunch for four is $52. This group of friends wants to give a 20% tip. How much money should the tip be?

3. Mrs. Sanders took a taxi to the airport to go on a business trip. She wanted to give the driver a 20% tip. The ride to the airport cost $11. How much will the tip be?

4. The Nguyen family had dinner at a restaurant and wanted to leave a 15% tip. The cost of the meal was $38. How much will the tip be?

Solve. Explain the method you used and why you chose that method.

5. The lunch special at a diner is soup and a salad. The special costs $6. Otis ordered one lunch special and plans to leave a 15% tip. How much money should the tip be?

6. The price of a haircut at a barbershop is $12. Ben plans to give the barber a 20% tip. How much money should the tip be?

LEARN

Percent of a Number (C)

Calculate Taxes

Worked Examples

You can find a percent of a number to calculate the sales tax on a purchase.

Facts about taxes: Buyers pay sales tax to a government when they buy an item. Sales tax is a percent of a dollar. Different governments set different sales tax percents, so sales tax percents, or rates, vary from state to state and city to city. To find the amount of sales tax you need to pay, a store will multiply the sales tax percent by the dollar amount of your purchase. You pay the amount of the purchase plus the sales tax.

PROBLEM 1 Janelle bought a pair of shoes for $29. The sales tax is 4%. How much sales tax will Janelle pay?

SOLUTION Finding a sales tax amount is just like finding the percent of a number. Write 4% as a decimal number and multiply by the shoe price.

$0.04 \times 29 = 1.16$

ANSWER Janelle will pay $1.16 in sales tax.

PROBLEM 2 With sales tax included, how much will Janelle's total cost for the pair of shoes be?

SOLUTION

1 Remember that you found the sales tax amount will be $1.16.

2 Add the sales tax to the purchase price.

$29 + 1.16 = 30.16$

ANSWER Janelle's total cost for the shoes will be $30.16.

LEARN

Solve.

1. The price of a sweatshirt is $20. The sales tax is 10%. What is the cost of the tax?

2. A family is buying books at a bookstore. The books cost $50. The sales tax is 12%. Find the amount of the tax and the total cost of the books and tax.

3. Tanya is buying a backpack for $15. The sales tax is 9%. How much will Tanya pay for the sales tax?

4. A scooter is on sale for $40. The sales tax is 8%. What is the cost of the sales tax?

5. Ryan wants to buy a new cell phone for $30. The sales tax is 10%. How much will Ryan pay for the cell phone including the sales tax?

6. The price of a T-shirt is $12. The sales tax is 8%. What is the total cost of the T-shirt including the sales tax?

7. Sam is buying a baseball glove for $18. The sales tax is 5%. What is the cost of the sales tax?

8. Blue jeans are on sale for $25. The sales tax is 10%. What is the cost of the sales tax?

LEARN

Represent Probabilities

Different Ways to Show Probability

Worked Examples

You can find the probability of a spinner landing on a certain color.

PROBLEM 1 What is the probability of this spinner landing on blue?

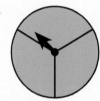

SOLUTION

1. Count the number of sections on the spinner. There are 3 equal-sized sections.

2. Count the number of sections for each color. The spinner has 3 blue sections.

3. Divide 3 blue sections by 3 total sections. Write the problem as a fraction: $\frac{3}{3}$. You can also write this probability as a decimal number and a percent.

ANSWER The probability of landing on blue is $\frac{3}{3} = 1.0 = 100\%$.

PROBLEM 2 What is the probability of this spinner landing on blue?

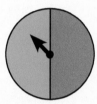

SOLUTION

1. Count the number of sections on the spinner. There are 2 equal-sized sections.

2. Count the number of sections for each color. The spinner has 1 red section and 1 blue section.

3. The question asks for the probability of landing on blue, so divide 1 blue section by 2 total sections. Write the problem as a fraction: $\frac{1}{2}$. You can also write this probability as a decimal number and a percent.

ANSWER The probability of landing on blue is $\frac{1}{2} = 0.5 = 50\%$.

Use the spinner to answer the question. Write the probability as a fraction, a decimal number, and a percent.

1. What is the probability of landing on red?

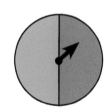

2. What is the probability of landing on purple?

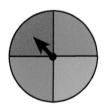

LEARN

3. What is the probability of landing on green?

4. What is the probability of landing on blue?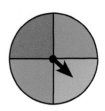

Read the problem and follow the directions.

5. Suppose you have this collection of socks in a basket. You pull out one sock from this basket without looking at the socks. What is the probability that you have pulled out a purple sock? Explain your answer. Express the probability as a fraction, a decimal, and a percent.

Worked Examples

You can find the probability of rolling a certain number on a number cube.

PROBLEM What is the probability of rolling a 3 on a number cube that has sides numbered 1, 2, 3, 4, 5, and 6? Express the probability as a fraction.

SOLUTION Each side has an equal chance of showing face up after the cube is rolled. The probability of rolling a 3 on the number cube is $\frac{1}{6}$ because a 3 is on 1 side out of the total 6 sides.

ANSWER The probability of rolling a 3 is $\frac{1}{6}$.

Find the probability and explain your answer. The number cubes have sides numbered 1, 2, 3, 4, 5, and 6.

6. What is the probability of rolling an odd number? Explain your answer. Express the probability as a fraction, a decimal number, and a percent.

   Hint: Think of which numbers on the sides of the number cube are odd.

7. What is the probability of rolling a 4 or a 6? Express your answer as a fraction in simplest form.

8. What is the probability of rolling a 1, 2, 3, 4, or 5? Express your answer as a fraction.

LEARN

Identify Dependent and Independent Events

Dependent and Independent Events

Solve.

1. The numbers 1, 2, 3, 4, 5, and 6 are on a number cube. Linda rolls a 4. If Linda rolls the number cube a second time, she wonders what the probability of rolling a 4 again will be. Are these events dependent or independent? Why?

2. A spinner has 8 equal-sized sections. There are 3 red sections and 5 yellow sections. When Marco spins, the pointer stops on a yellow section. If Marco spins a second time, he wonders what the probability of stopping on a different yellow section will be. Are these events dependent or independent? Why?

3. Lisa has 10 index cards. She numbers them 1 through 10. She mixes the cards up and places them face down on a table. She picks a 6 and does not put the card back on the table. Then she picks a 9. Are these events dependent or independent? Why?

4. Percy spells out his hometown with tiles: PALOMA. He mixes up the tiles and places them face down on a table. Percy picks an A. He does not return the tile to the table. He picks a tile from the table again. This time he gets a P. Are these events dependent or independent? Why?

5. There are 4 yellow paper clips, 2 green paper clips, and 6 white paper clips in a box. Ken takes a paper clip out of the box without looking. He gets a green paper clip. Ken does not put the green paper clip back in the box. He takes a paper clip out of the box again without looking. This time he gets a white paper clip. Are these events dependent or independent? Explain.

TRY IT

Choose the answer.

6. The numbers 1, 2, 3, 4, 5, and 6 are on the sides of a number cube. Rebecca rolled a 5. Then she rolled a 6. Are these events dependent or independent?

    A. dependent   B. independent

7. A bag had 14 bagels in it. In the bag, 10 of the bagels were wheat and 4 were plain. Julie reached in and randomly pulled out a wheat bagel. She did not put it back. She reached in and took another bagel. Are these events dependent or independent?

    A. dependent   B. independent

8. Dixie has 8 quarters and 15 dimes in her change purse. She reaches in and randomly pulls out a quarter. She puts the quarter back into her change purse and then reaches in and pulls out another coin. Are these events dependent or independent?

    A. dependent   B. independent

9. Which situation shows dependent events?

    A. Howard rolls a number cube and tosses a coin.

    B. David has a bag with 5 orange marbles and 4 red marbles. He picks a marble, looks at the color, and puts the marble back into the bag. Then he picks a second marble.

    C. Julia has 10 red grapes and 6 green grapes in a bowl. Without looking at the grapes, she picks one and eats it. She then picks another grape.

    D. Laura tosses a coin and it shows heads. She tosses the coin again.

10. Which situation shows independent events?

    A. Darrell has 8 white socks and 8 blue socks in a drawer. He picks a sock from a drawer, and then he picks another sock without putting the first sock back in the drawer.

    B. Daniela wrote the numbers 1 through 13 on pieces of paper. She put them into a bag and randomly pulled out the paper with 13 on it. She did not replace it and then randomly selected another one.

    C. Bettina has 3 white tennis skirts and 5 pink tennis skirts. She randomly picks a skirt from her closet and then picks another one without putting the first one back.

    D. Hugh has 6 dimes and 7 nickels in his pocket. He reaches in and randomly pulls out a dime. He replaces the coin and then reaches in and pulls out another coin.

TRY IT

11. Which situation shows dependent events?

  A. Sandy rolls a number cube and tosses a coin.

  B. Tamsin has 20 black olives and 13 green olives in a bowl. Without looking at the olives, Tamsin picks one and eats it. She then picks another olive.

  C. Delia wrote the numbers 1 through 15 on separate pieces of paper. She put them into a bag and randomly pulled out the paper with 12 on it. She put it back and then randomly selected another one.

  D. Molly tosses a coin and it shows heads. She tosses the coin again.

12. Which situation shows independent events?

  A. Debbie has a box of muffins. In the box, 10 of the muffins are cranberry and 12 are banana. Debbie reached in and randomly pulled out a cranberry muffin. She did not put it back. Then she reached in and took another muffin.

  B. Tom had a bag of paper clips. He had 25 large and 19 small paper clips. He reached into the bag and randomly pulled out a small paper clip. Without replacing it, he pulled out another paper clip.

  C. Eva had a bag of cubes. She had 19 blue cubes and 10 red cubes. She reached into the bag and randomly pulled out a blue cube. She replaced it and then reached in and pulled out another cube.

  D. Kate has a bag with 12 cans of soup in it. In the bag, 6 of the cans of soup are potato and 6 are mushroom. Kate reaches into the bag without looking and pulls out a can of mushroom soup. She does not put it back. She reaches back into the bag for another can of soup.

TRY IT

Probability and Predictions

Make Predictions

Worked Examples

You can use theoretical probability to make predictions. Theoretical probability is the kind of probability given to events that should occur in a perfect experiment.

PROBLEM 1 A bag contains 11 pink erasers, 6 blue erasers, 6 white erasers, and 1 yellow eraser. If you randomly pick 1 eraser from the bag, is it certain, likely, unlikely, or impossible that the eraser will be yellow?

SOLUTION

1. Find out how many erasers are in the bag by adding the numbers of erasers in the problem: $11 + 6 + 6 + 1 = 24$.

2. Since the problem says that 1 eraser is yellow, write the probability of picking a yellow eraser as a fraction: $\frac{1}{24}$.

3. Think about the probability of picking a yellow eraser.
   - It is not impossible since the probability is greater than 0.
   - It is not certain since the probability is less than 1.
   - It is not likely since there is only 1 chance out of 24 chances that you would pick a yellow eraser.

ANSWER The probability of picking a yellow eraser is unlikely.

PROBLEM 2 After 40 spins, the spinner will theoretically have landed on green 10 times. Predict the number of times the spinner would land on green in the next 32 spins.

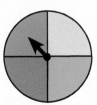

SOLUTION Each section of the spinner has the same probability, $\frac{1}{4}$. After 40 spins, the theoretical probability is $\frac{1}{4}$ or $\frac{10}{40}$. The spinner can be expected to land on each section 10 times.

You can also find the theoretical probability of how many times the spinner would land on green in 32 spins.

$$\frac{1}{4} = \frac{?}{32}$$

$$\frac{1}{4} = \frac{8}{32}$$

ANSWER The number of times the spinner will land on green is predicted to be 8.

LEARN

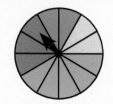

PROBLEM 3 Reina spins this spinner 18 times. Which color will the spinner most likely point to the most number of times?

SOLUTION Count the sections on the spinner by color. There are more blue sections than sections of any other color.

ANSWER The spinner will most likely point to a blue section the most number of times.

Read the story problem. Answer whether the probability is certain, likely, unlikely, or impossible.

There are 14 red jelly beans, 4 blue jelly beans, and 2 green jelly beans in a jar.

1. If 1 jelly bean is randomly picked from the jar, how likely is it that the jelly bean will be yellow?

2. If 1 jelly bean is randomly picked from the jar, what is the probability that it jelly bean will be red?

3. If 1 jelly bean is randomly picked from the jar, what is the probability that the jelly bean will be blue?

4. If 1 jelly bean is randomly picked from the jar, what is the probability that the jelly bean will be green?

Solve. Explain the answer by writing equivalent fractions.

5. After 24 spins, the spinner will theoretically have landed on yellow 6 times. Predict how many times the spinner would land on yellow in the next 36 spins.

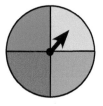

LEARN

Choose the answer.

6. Abby has a bag of blocks. She knows that each block is either purple or green. She pulls a block from the bag and records the color on a chart. She puts the block back into the bag and pulls out another block. After Abby has pulled out 10 blocks, her tally chart looks like this. Which prediction about the blocks in the bag is likely?

Blocks in Abby's Bag	
Purple	**Green**
~~IIII~~ II	III

A. There are more green blocks than purple blocks in the bag.

B. There are more purple blocks than green blocks in the bag.

C. The number of purple blocks in the bag is equal to the number of green blocks.

Worked Examples

You can use experimental probability to make predictions. Experimental probability is the kind of probability given to events that occur during an actual experiment. You use data to measure the chance of an event happening.

PROBLEM The chart shows the type and number of birds that scientists counted near a river and lake on a one-day bird-counting project each year for 5 years. Predict which type of bird would be the most numerous in Year 6.

Bird Survey						
Type of Bird	**Year 1**	**Year 2**	**Year 3**	**Year 4**	**Year 5**	**Year 6**
Sparrow	12	14	10	15	13	?
Woodpecker	2	4	5	5	4	?
Duck	10	8	16	18	19	?
Hawk	3	2	1	3	4	?

SOLUTION Observe the trends in the chart.

ANSWER You can predict that ducks will be the most numerous birds in the sixth year of the bird-counting project because the greatest number of birds in the first 5 years are ducks. The number of ducks has also increased for the past 3 years.

L E A R N

Read the problem and follow the directions.

7. The owner of a movie rental business made this chart to show the different types of movies rented each week by customers. Using the results from Weeks 1–4, predict the type of movie that the greatest number of customers will likely rent in Week 5.

Movie Rentals					
Type	Week 1	Week 2	Week 3	Week 4	Week 5
Drama	83	78	91	75	?
Comedy	56	79	49	53	?
Adventure	156	139	147	155	?
Mystery	22	31	28	33	?

8. The chart shows the number of points a basketball team scored in Games 1–4. Predict the number of points the team will likely score in Game 5 and explain your reasoning.

Basketball Scores					
	Game 1	Game 2	Game 3	Game 4	Game 5
Points	78	82	73	80	?

LEARN

Probability and Predictions

Prediction Problems

Read the problem and follow the directions.

1. A spinner has 4 equal-sized sections. One section is orange; one section is blue; one section is green; and one section is red. After 12 spins, the spinner will theoretically have landed on red 3 times. Predict the number of times the spinner will land on red in the next 8 spins. Explain your answer.

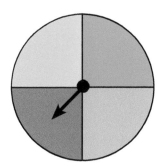

2. A spinner has 3 equal-sized sections. One section is orange; one section is green; and one section is blue. After 36 spins, the spinner will theoretically have landed on green 12 times. Predict the number of times the spinner will land on green in the next 15 spins. Explain your answer.

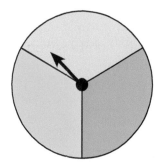

3. The owner of an online T-shirt store made this chart to show the number of customers who bought different sizes of T-shirts. Based on the results from Weeks 1–4, predict the size of T-shirts that the fewest number of customers will buy in Week 5.

T-Shirt Sales					
Size	Week 1	Week 2	Week 3	Week 4	Week 5
Small	114	120	99	125	?
Medium	34	37	33	41	?
Large	225	218	199	189	?
X-Large	150	177	179	164	?

TRY IT

Choose the answer.

4. There are 25 gold stars, 15 red stars, and 3 blue stars in a box. If Fiona randomly picks 1 star from the box, what is the probability that the star will be gold?

    A. certain   B. likely   C. unlikely   D. impossible

5. There are 20 orange balls and 3 green balls in a bag. Paige reaches into the bag and pulls out a ball. What is the probability that the ball is green?

    A. certain   B. likely   C. unlikely   D. impossible

6. There are exactly 12 cranberry muffins and no other types of muffins in a box. Tara randomly picks 1 muffin from the box. What is the probability that the muffin will be a bran muffin?

    A. certain   B. likely   C. unlikely   D. impossible

7. The owner of a bakery made this chart showing the number of muffins she sold each week. Predict which type of muffin would sell the most in Week 4.

Muffins Sold				
Flavor	Week 1	Week 2	Week 3	Week 4
Orange	88	82	79	?
Bran	56	50	51	?
Blueberry	38	40	37	?
Banana Nut	11	10	13	?

    A. orange   B. bran   C. blueberry   D. banana nut

8. Olivia spun a spinner 30 times and recorded the results. If Olivia spins her spinner another 15 times, which color will the spinner most likely land on? Base your answer on the information in the chart.

    A. red

    B. green

    C. yellow

    D. orange

Spinner Results	
Red	6
Green	12
Yellow	5
Orange	7

Use the Distributive Property (A)

Apply the Distributive Property

You can use the distributive property to evaluate expressions.

PROBLEM 1 Use the distributive property to evaluate this expression:

$$3 \cdot 42$$

SOLUTION

1 Change 42 to the expression $40 + 2$, so you have numbers that are easy to multiply with. Substitute $(40 + 2)$ into the original expression.

$$3 \cdot 42 = 3 \cdot (40 + 2)$$

2 Use the distributive property. Write $(3 \cdot 40)$ and $(3 \cdot 2)$ below $3 \cdot (40 + 2)$. Write an addition sign between the two expressions. The distributive property says that you will get the same answer whether you multiply a number by a sum (such as 42) or multiply the number by each addend of the sum (such as 40 and 2) and then add the products.

$$3 \cdot 42 = 3 \cdot (40 + 2)$$
$$= (3 \cdot 40) + (3 \cdot 2)$$

3 Use the order of operations to do the operations inside parentheses first.

$$3 \cdot 42 = 3 \cdot (40 + 2)$$
$$= (3 \cdot 40) + (3 \cdot 2)$$
$$= 120 + 6$$

4 Use the order of operations to add 120 and 6 next.

$$3 \cdot 42 = 3 \cdot (40 + 2)$$
$$= (3 \cdot 40) + (3 \cdot 2)$$
$$= 120 + 6$$
$$= 126$$

5 Check your work by applying the order of operations to the expression you used in Step 1.

$$3 \cdot 42 = 3 \cdot (40 + 2) = 126$$

ANSWER The value of $3 \cdot 42$ is 126.

LEARN

PROBLEM 2 Find the value of *f* that makes this equation true:

$$6 \cdot 78 = (6 \cdot f) + (6 \cdot 8)$$

SOLUTION

1 Use the distributive property to find the value of *f*. The distributive property says that you will get the same answer whether you multiply a number by a sum (such as 78) or multiply the number by each addend of the sum (*f* and 8) and then add the products.

When 78 has two addends and one of them is 8, what is the other addend? Subtract to find out.

$78 - 8 = 70$

So $70 + 8 = 78$.

2 Because $70 + 8$ equals 78, replace *f* with 70 to make the equation true.

$6 \cdot 78 = (6 \cdot 70) + (6 \cdot 8)$

ANSWER The value of *f* that makes the equation true is 70.

Use the distributive property to evaluate the expression. Show the steps you used to find the answer.

1. $94 \cdot 7$
2. $7 \cdot 51$
3. $9 \cdot (6 + b)$

Use the distributive property to find the value of the variable *w* that makes the equation true. Show the steps you used to find the answer.

4. $8 \cdot 67 = (8 \cdot w) + (8 \cdot 7)$

Read the problem and follow the directions.

5. Katie is having 7 friends over to lunch. She is giving each of them 3 chicken tenders and some apple slices for lunch. Let *a* represent the unknown number of apple slices. Use the distributive property to write an expression in simplest form that represents the total number of food pieces Katie needs. Show the steps you used to find the answer.

6. Lou ran the 75-yard dash 3 times today before winning the final race. Use the distributive property to find out how many yards he ran.

LEARN

Use the Distributive Property (B)

Simplify with Distributive Property

Worked Examples

You can simplify expressions by applying the distributive property to an equation.

PROBLEM 1 Find the missing numbers.

$$6 \cdot (9 - 4) = (6 \cdot 9) - (6 \cdot 4)$$
$$6 \cdot ? = ? - ?$$
$$? = ?$$

SOLUTION

1 Work through the *left side* of the equation first.
- Simplify the problem in parentheses. $9 - 4 = 5$, so $6 \cdot ?$ becomes $6 \cdot 5$.
- Multiply. $6 \cdot 5 = 30$, so $? = ?$ becomes $30 = ?$

2 Work through the *right side* of the equation next.
- Simplify the first problem in parentheses. $6 \cdot 9 = 54$
- Simplify the second problem in parentheses. $6 \cdot 4 = 24$
- So $? - ?$ becomes $54 - 24$. $54 - 24$
- Subtract. $54 - 24 = 30$
- So $30 = ?$ becomes $30 = 30$. $30 = 30$

ANSWER
$$6 \cdot (9 - 4) = (6 \cdot 9) - (6 \cdot 4)$$
$$6 \cdot 5 = 54 - 24$$
$$30 = 30$$

L E A R N

PROBLEM 2 Find the missing number or variable to replace the question mark in the expression on the right side of this equation:

$$7 \cdot (x + 8) = 7 \cdot ? + 7 \cdot 8$$

SOLUTION The distributive property says that you will get the same answer whether you multiply a number by a sum or multiply the number by each addend of the sum and then add the products.

The left side of the equation shows 7 multiplied by a sum, $x + 8$. The right side will be equal to the left side if the 7 is multiplied by each addend, x and 8, and the two products are then added.

If the ? on the right side is replaced with an x, then the two sides of the equation will equal each other under the distributive property.

Reminder: You'll sometimes see expressions that do not have parentheses to indicate which operation to do first, such as $7 \cdot ? + 7 \cdot 8$. The order of operations tells you to first complete the multiplication and division from left to right. Then complete the addition and subtraction from left to right.

ANSWER The variable x should replace the question mark.

$$7 \cdot (x + 8) = 7 \cdot x + 7 \cdot 8$$

PROBLEM 3 Find the missing number or variable to replace the question mark on the right side of this equation:

$$4 \cdot (m - 2) = (4 \cdot ?) - (4 \cdot 2)$$

SOLUTION If an expression that uses subtraction is being multiplied by a number, the distributive property says that you will get the same answer whether you multiply the number by the difference or multiply the number by each number in the subtraction expression and then subtract.

If the ? on the right side is replaced with the variable m, then the two sides of the equation will equal each other under the distributive property.

ANSWER The variable m should replace the question mark.

$$4 \cdot (m - 2) = (4 \cdot m) - (4 \cdot 2)$$

PROBLEM 4 Use the distributive property to simplify.

$$4 \cdot (7 - 5)$$

SOLUTION
$$4 \cdot (7 - 5) = 4(7) - 4(5)$$
$$= 28 - 20$$
$$= 8$$

ANSWER $4 \cdot (7 - 5) = 8$

LEARN

Find the missing numbers or expressions.

1. $5 \cdot (3 + 6) = (5 \cdot 3) + (5 \cdot 6)$

    $5 \cdot \underline{\ ?\ } = \underline{\ ?\ } + 30$

    $\underline{\ ?\ } = \underline{\ ?\ }$

2. $7 \cdot (5 + 1) = (7 \cdot 5) + (7 \cdot 1)$

    $\underline{\ ?\ } \cdot 6 = 35 + \underline{\ ?\ }$

    $\underline{\ ?\ } = \underline{\ ?\ }$

3. $8 \cdot (4 - 2) = (8 \cdot 4) - (8 \cdot 2)$

    $\underline{\ ?\ } \cdot \underline{\ ?\ } = \underline{\ ?\ } - \underline{\ ?\ }$

    $\underline{\ ?\ } = \underline{\ ?\ }$

4. $5 \cdot (6 - t) = (5 \cdot 6) - (5 \cdot t)$

    $5 \cdot (6 - t) = \underline{\ ?\ } - (5t)$

    $5 \cdot (6 - t) = \underline{\ ?\ }$

Find the missing number or variable.

5. $4 \cdot (6 - 2) = (4 \cdot 6) - (4 \cdot \underline{\ ?\ })$

6. $3 \cdot (\underline{\ ?\ } - 4) = (3 \cdot 9) - (3 \cdot 4)$

7. $2 \cdot (\underline{\ ?\ } - f) = (2 \cdot 5) - (2 \cdot f)$

8. $6 \cdot (b + 2) = (6 \cdot \underline{\ ?\ }) + (6 \cdot 2)$

Use the distributive property to simplify.

9. $6 \cdot (3 + 2) = \underline{\ ?\ }$

10. $4 \cdot (7 + 1) = \underline{\ ?\ }$

11. $5 \cdot (7 - 2) = \underline{\ ?\ }$

12. $9 \cdot (3 - 2) = \underline{\ ?\ }$

LEARN

One Variable in Algebraic Expressions

Use Substitution in Expressions

You can substitute a number for a variable to evaluate an expression. This process is known as *evaluating using substitution,* or simply *substitution.*

PROBLEM 1 Find the value of this expression by substituting 2 for m:

$$19m$$

SOLUTION $19m = 19 \cdot 2$

$$= 38$$

Notice that this expression had one operation, multiplication. When 2 was substituted for the variable m, 19 was multiplied by 2.

ANSWER The value of the expression $19m$ is 38 when 2 is substituted for m.

PROBLEM 2 Find the value of this expression by substituting 2 for p:

$$7p + 8$$

SOLUTION $7p + 8 = 7 \cdot 2 + 8$

$$= 14 + 8$$

$$= 22$$

Notice that when 2 replaced p, the expression became $7 \cdot 2 + 8$. By the order of operations, the first step was to multiply, and the next step was to add.

ANSWER The value of the expression $7p + 8$ is 22 when 2 is substituted for p.

LEARN

PROBLEM 3 Find the value of this expression by substituting 3 for n:

$$(5 + n) - 2$$

SOLUTION
$$
\begin{aligned}
(5 + n) - 2 &= (5 + 3) - 2 \\
&= 8 - 2 \\
&= 6
\end{aligned}
$$

Notice that the expression had two operations, addition and subtraction. The addition was in parentheses, so it was calculated first. Then the subtraction was calculated.

ANSWER The value of the expression $(5 + n) - 2$ is 6 when 3 is substituted for n.

PROBLEM 4 Find the value of this expression by substituting 4 for y:

$$8 \cdot 3 \div (2 + y)$$

SOLUTION
$$
\begin{aligned}
8 \cdot 3 \div (2 + y) &= 8 \cdot 3 \div (2 + 4) \\
&= 8 \cdot 3 \div 6 \\
&= 24 \div 6 \\
&= 4
\end{aligned}
$$

Notice that the expression had three operations, multiplication, division, and addition. The addition was calculated first because it was in parentheses. The multiplication was calculated second because the order of operations says to do multiplication and division from left to right. The division was calculated last because it was to the right of the multiplication.

ANSWER The value of the expression $8 \cdot 3 \div (2 + y)$ is 4 when 4 is substituted for y.

Find the value of the expression.

1. Substitute 25 for y.
   $6y$

2. Substitute 12 for g.
   $(27 - g) + 34$

3. Substitute 33 for k.
   $(22 + k) \div 5$

4. Substitute 7 for r.
   $(6 - 3) \cdot 5 + r$

5. Substitute 4 for d.
   $7 + 20 - (12 \div d)$

6. Substitute 12 for j.
   $(3 + j) \cdot 3 \div 9$

LEARN

Expression and Equation Problems (A)

Expressions and Story Problems

Worked Examples

You can write an expression with a variable to represent a story problem.

PROBLEM Anna's mom buys 3 bags that contain an equal number of wrapped cheese slices. The number of cheese slices in each bag is not known. What expression describes the total number of cheese slices?

SOLUTION Divide to solve the problem. Use the method that is easiest for you. One way is shown below.

1 Identify what you know and what you don't know. You know that Anna's mom bought 3 bags. You know that each bag has an equal number of wrapped cheese slices. You don't know how many wrapped cheese slices are in each bag.

2 Name a variable, such as c, and decide what the variable stands for. You don't know the number of wrapped cheese slices in each bag, so the variable c stands for that unknown number.

3 Decide if you need to add, subtract, multiply, or divide. In this problem, you would multiply 3 times the number of cheese slices to get the answer.

ANSWER The expression is $3 \cdot c$. You can also write that expression as $3c$.

Write the expression for the story problem. You may decide what letter to use as a variable.

1. Percy earned $16 mowing lawns. He plans to spend part of that money at the county fair. What expression describes how much money he will have after he leaves the county fair?

2. Rochelle picked some peppers. Her neighbor gave her 15 more peppers. What expression describes how many peppers she has?

3. Terrence had some baseball cards. He wanted to divide them into 5 equal groups. What expression describes how many baseball cards will be in each group?

Expression and Equation Problems (A)

Match Expressions and Story Problems

Worked Examples

You can show how an expression matches the details in the following story problem:

- Kim reads all the books her favorite author writes. On Wednesday, she checked out the author's newest book from the library and read 38 pages. On Thursday, she read more pages of the book. How many pages did Kim read in two days?

PROBLEM What does the expression $38 + p$ mean in relation to the story problem?

SOLUTION

1 Figure out what p stands for in the expression. It represents the unknown number of pages Kim read on Thursday. You do not know what that number is yet.

2 Figure out what $38 + p$ means. It means 38 pages plus an unknown number of pages.

3 Use the expression in an explanation of how it relates to the story problem.

ANSWER The expression $38 + p$ represents the number of pages Kim read on Wednesday and Thursday.

Explain what the variable and numbers in the given expression mean. Then explain how the given expression is related to the story problem.

1. $5c \div 3$

   Larry washed cars for $5 each. He donated the money he earned equally to 3 groups that help students go to college. How much money did Larry donate to each group?

2. $b - 2$

   Inez is hiking on a park trail that is measured in miles. She has hiked 2 miles so far. How many miles does Inez have to hike until she completes the entire trail?

3. $12b$

   David removed all the books from 12 shelves. Each shelf had the same number of books on it. How many books did David remove from shelves?

LEARN

You can write an expression to represent a story problem and then change the expression when the story problem changes.

- Bill brought an unknown number of baseball cards to a sports card show. He sold 7 baseball cards. What expression represents the number of baseball cards Bill has left?

PROBLEM 1 Write an expression for the story problem.

SOLUTION

1 Identify what you know. You know that Bill sold 7 baseball cards.

2 Identify what you don't know. You don't know how many baseball cards Bill brought to the sports card show. That unknown amount can be represented by the variable b.

3 Decide what operation you should use and write an expression with the variable b and the information you know.

ANSWER $b - 7$

PROBLEM 2 Extend Problem 1. What expression represents the number of baseball cards Bill has left if he sells 2 more cards?

SOLUTION

1 Add $7 + 2$ because he sold 7 cards and then 2 more cards.

2 Replace the 7 with a 9 in the expression.

ANSWER $b - 9$

PROBLEM 3 Caron had some milk boxes at home. She bought 4 more milk boxes. She could represent the number of milk boxes she has now by using the expression $m + 4$. What expression represents the number of milk boxes she has if she buys another 9 milk boxes?

SOLUTION

1 Write $4 + 9$ because you know that Caron bought 4 milk boxes and then 9 more milk boxes. Add.

$4 + 9 = 13$

2 Replace the 4 in the original expression, $m + 4$, with 13.

ANSWER $m + 13$

LEARN

Explain what information you know and what information you don't know from reading the story problem. Then write an expression that represents the story problem.

4. Adam has 5 baskets and a pile of onions. He wants to put the same number of onions in each basket. What expression represents how many onions he should put in each basket?

Write an expression that represents the changed story problem.

5. Jerry has some ears of corn from his corn plants. He gave away 10 ears of corn. He could use the expression $c - 10$ for the amount of corn he gave away. If he then ate 3 ears of corn, what expression represents the number of ears of corn remaining?

6. A garden had some rows of beans. A deer ate 2 rows of beans. An expression that represents how many rows of beans were left is $g - 2$. If another deer ate 2 more rows of beans, what expression represents the number of rows of beans remaining?

LEARN

Expression and Equation Problems (A)

Practice with Expressions

Choose the answer.

1. Becky made beaded necklaces. She put 8 beads on each necklace. She could use the expression $8 \cdot n$ to represent the number of beads she used to make n necklaces.

   Which expression represents the number of beads Becky could use if she put 4 more beads on each necklace?

   A. $12 \cdot 4$

   B. $8 \cdot 4$

   C. $4 \cdot n$

   D. $12 \cdot n$

2. Randy bought several postcards when he was on vacation. He mailed 5 of the postcards to his friends. He could use the expression $p - 5$ to represent the number of postcards he has left.

   Which expression represents the number of postcards Randy has left if he sends 3 more postcards to friends?

   A. $p - 3$

   B. $p - 8$

   C. $5 - 3$

   D. $8 - 5$

3. Jennifer can do 6 fewer sit-ups than Michelle. Jennifer described the number of sit-ups she can do using the expression $m - 6$.

   One day Jennifer was tired and did 2 fewer sit-ups than usual. Which expression represents the number of sit-ups Jennifer did that day?

   A. $6 - 2$

   B. $m - 4$

   C. $m - 6$

   D. $m - 8$

4. Beth bought 2 packages of coloring markers. She could use the expression $2m$ to represent the total number of coloring markers she bought.

   Which expression represents the total number of coloring markers Beth would have if she bought 5 more packages of coloring markers?

   A. 2×7

   B. 2×5

   C. $7m$

   D. $5m$

5. Pedro rented some movies on Saturday. He returned 1 movie on Monday. He could use the expression $m - 1$ to represent the number of movies he has left.

   Which expression represents the number of movies Pedro has left if he returns 2 more movies?

   A. $m - 2$

   B. $m - 3$

   C. $3 - 2$

   D. $2 - 1$

6. Jeffrey had some apples at home. He bought 6 more apples. He could represent the number of apples that he now has by using the expression $a + 6$.

   Which expression represents the number of apples Jeffrey has if he buys another 8 apples?

   A. $a + 6$

   B. $a + 14$

   C. $6 + 8$

   D. $6 + 14$

TRY IT

7. Megan worked 10 hours overtime in one month. She could use the expression $t + 10$ to represent the total time she worked.

   Which expression represents the total number of hours Megan worked if she had worked an additional 12 hours overtime?

   A. $t + 2$ B. $t + 10$

   C. $2 + 12$ D. $t + 22$

8. Peter has 4 fewer trophies than Jack. Peter can represent the number of trophies he has with the expression $t - 4$.

   Peter won another 2 trophies. Which expression represents the number of trophies Peter has now?

   A. $t - 2$ B. $t - 4$

   C. $t - 6$ D. $t - 10$

9. Carla had several jigsaw puzzles. She bought 6 more jigsaw puzzles. She could use the expression $p + 6$ to represent the number of jigsaw puzzles she has now.

   Which expression represents the number of jigsaw puzzles Carla has if she buys 4 more jigsaw puzzles?

   A. $10 + 4$ B. $p + 4$

   C. $6 + 4$ D. $p + 10$

10. Anna had some peaches at home. She bought 5 more peaches. She could represent the number of peaches that she now has by using the expression $p + 5$.

    Which expression represents the number of peaches Anna has if she buys another 3 peaches?

    A. $p + 3$ B. $p + 5$

    C. $p + 8$ D. $3 + 5$

11. Jason bought a number of packages of buns. There are 8 buns in each package. He could use the expression $8b$ to represent the number of buns he bought.

    Which expression would represent the number of buns Jason bought if the store had put an additional 2 buns into each package?

    A. 10×8 B. $2b$

    C. 2×8 D. $10b$

12. Edgar has a pack of stickers to share with his 4 friends. He could represent the number of stickers each friend would get using the expression $s \div 4$.

    Edgar is thinking of sharing his stickers with 1 additional friend. Which expression would represent the number of stickers each person would get now?

    A. $s \div 1$ B. $s \div 3$

    C. $s \div 5$ D. $4 + 1$

13. Paul paid $5 per ticket for a number of tickets to the baseball game on Wednesday. He could represent the total he spent on baseball tickets by using the expression $5t$.

    On Saturday, Paul bought the same number of tickets. However, the price of these tickets was $2 more per ticket. Which expression represents the amount Paul paid for tickets on Saturday?

    A. 5×2 B. $2t$

    C. $7t$ D. $10t$

14. Eddie has a set of football cards he wants to put in an album. He is planning on putting 9 cards per page. He could represent the number of pages he would need by using the expression $b \div 9$.

    Eddie is thinking of putting 5 fewer cards on each page. Which expression would represent the number of pages he would need?

    A. $b \div 4$ B. $b \div 5$

    C. $b \div 14$ D. $b \div 45$

T R Y   I T

Expression and Equation Problems (B)

Equations and Story Problems

Worked Examples

You can write an equation for a story problem.

PROBLEM A painter uses 2.5 gallons of paint to cover the walls in 1 room of a building. He needs to paint a total of 6 rooms in the building. Each room is the same size. What equation describes the number of gallons of paint the painter will need to finish the job?

SOLUTION Multiply to solve the problem. Use the method that is easiest for you. One way is shown below.

1 Identify what you know. You know that 2.5 gallons of paint are needed for 1 room. You know the painter will paint 6 rooms of equal size.

2 Identify what you don't know. You don't know the total number of gallons of paint needed to finish the job.

3 Name a variable, such as p, and decide what the variable stands for. You don't know the total number of gallons of paint needed, so the variable p stands for that unknown number.

4 Write an equation to show what the problem has told you. Because the painter is painting 6 rooms and needs 2.5 gallons of paint per room, you know you need to multiply. The variable will stand for the product.

ANSWER $2.5 \times 6 = p$, or $6 \times 2.5 = p$

Write an equation for the story problem. You may decide what letter to use as a variable.

1. Meredith used 54 seashells to decorate 6 picture frames. She put an equal number of seashells on each frame. What equation describes the number of seashells Meredith put on each picture frame?

2. Harry walked to the library and back home for a total of 1.25 miles. If he walked that route every day for 8 days, how many miles will he have walked?

LEARN

Expression and Equation Problems (B)

Match Equations and Story Problems

You can show how an equation matches the details in the following story problem:

- A scientist records data about wolves she is tracking. She knows there are 45 wolves in the area. She observes 22 of the wolves at a pond one day. The scientist wants to know how many wolves were not at the pond that day.

PROBLEM How can $45 - w = 22$ be matched with the details in the story problem?

SOLUTION

1 Decide what w stands for in the equation. It stands for the unknown number of wolves that weren't at the pond that day.

2 Decide what $45 - w$ means. It means 45 minus an unknown number of wolves.

3 Decide what 22 means. It means the number of wolves the scientist observed at the pond.

ANSWER The equation $45 - w = 22$ represents the number of wolves that weren't at the pond that day.

Explain what the variable and numbers in the given equation mean. Then explain how the given equation is related to the story problem.

1. $10 + 3c = 34$

    Linda had 10 comic books. She bought 3 boxes of comic books at a yard sale. Each box has the same number of comic books. Now Linda has 34 comic books. How many comic books are in each box?

2. $60 \div d = 3$

    Kelly bought 60 pounds of dry dog food. The dog food is in 3 equal-sized bags. How many pounds of dog food are in each bag?

L E A R N

You can write an equation to represent a story problem and then change the equation when the story problem changes.

- Raul planted a flower garden. He planted 6 geraniums and 8 petunias in one row. How many flowers did Raul plant in one row?

PROBLEM 1 Write an equation for the story problem.

SOLUTION

1 Identify what you know. You know that Raul planted 6 geraniums and 8 petunias in one row.

2 Identify what you don't know. You don't know how many flowers Raul planted in one row. That unknown amount can be called variable f.

3 Decide which operation you should use, and write an equation with the variable f and the information you know.

ANSWER $6 + 8 = f$

PROBLEM 2 Extend the problem. What equation represents the total number of flowers Raul planted if he planted 3 rows that had 6 geraniums and 8 petunias in each row?

SOLUTION

1 Let the variable f represent the total number.

2 Show that $6 + 8$ is being multiplied by 3 by writing $3 \cdot (6 + 8)$.

3 Replace the expression $6 + 8$ with $3 \cdot (6 + 8)$ in the equation.

ANSWER $3 \cdot (6 + 8) = f$

PROBLEM 3 Sherman helped on park cleanup day and collected 9 pounds of cans and 6 pounds of bottles. He wrote this equation to represent the unknown total number of pounds of items he collected.

$9 + 6 = p$

He wanted to divide those items into 3 equal groups. Write an equation that represents the number of items in each group.

SOLUTION Show $9 + 6$ as an expression that is divided by 3.

ANSWER $(9 + 6) \div 3 = p$

L E A R N

Explain what information you know and what information you don't know from reading the story problem. Then write an equation that represents the story problem.

3. Aisha wrote 12 poems during the summer. If she wrote 12 poems each in the fall, spring, and winter, how many poems will she have written altogether?

Write an equation that represents the changed story problem.

4. Colton had 30 T-shirts and pairs of pants. He gave away 14 of those items that were too small. He wrote this equation to represent the items of clothing he gave away: $30 - 14 = c$.

   He then found another T-shirt and didn't give it away. What equation represents the total number of items of clothing he had after he gave away some items and found the T-shirt?

5. Annie had 17 notebooks and gave 5 of the notebooks to her sister. She wrote this equation to represent the number of notebooks she had left: $17 - 5 = n$.

   She decided to sort her notebooks into 3 stacks. What equation represents the number of notebooks in each stack?

LEARN

Expression and Equation Problems (B)

Practice with Equations

Choose the answer.

1. Tara did 3 hours of math practice and 4 hours of social studies reading in one week. She wrote the following equation to represent the total number of hours, h, of math practice and reading she did: $h = 3 + 4$.

   Tara expects to have 3 hours of math practice and 4 hours of social studies reading each week for the next 5 weeks. Now let the variable h represent the total number of hours of homework Tara will have. Which equation represents the total number of hours of work she will have in the next 5 weeks?

   A. $h = 3 + 4$

   B. $h = 3 \times 4 \times 5$

   C. $h = 3 + 4 + 5$

   D. $h = 5 \cdot (3 + 4)$

2. Tess made 6 corn muffins and 12 bran muffins. She wrote the following equation to represent the total number of muffins, m, she made: $m = 6 + 12$.

   Tess stores an equal number of the total number of muffins she made in each of 3 small containers. Now let the variable m stand for the number of muffins in each container. Which equation represents the number of muffins in each container?

   A. $m = 6 + 12 + 3$

   B. $m = 6 + 12 - 3$

   C. $m = (6 + 12) \div 3$

   D. $m = (6 + 12) \times 3$

3. Nathan always reads 2 more books than he is required to read in a month. He could show the total number of books he reads in a month with the expression $b + 2$, where b represents the number of books he is required to read.

   Which expression represents the total number of books Nathan read in a month if he read an additional 5 books more than required that month?

   A. $b + 2$

   B. $2 + 5$

   C. $b + 7$

   D. $2 + 3$

TRY IT

4. Maria planned to read 9 fiction and 12 history books each month. She could show the total number of books she planned to read each month with the equation $b = 9 + 12$, where b represents the number of books Maria planned to read.

   Now let the variable b represent the total number of books Maria planned to read in 5 months. Which equation would represent the number of books Maria would read in 5 months?

   A. $b = 5 + (9 + 12)$

   B. $b = 5 \cdot (9 + 12)$

   C. $b = 9 + 12 \cdot 5$

   D. $b = 5 \cdot 9 + 12$

5. Ben had 15 stamps in his stamp collection. He sold 6 stamps. Ben wrote the following equation to represent the number of stamps he has left: $15 - 6 = t$. The variable t represents the total number of stamps Ben has left.

   Ben bought 7 more stamps. Now let the variable t stand for the total number of stamps Ben has now. Which equation represents the number of stamps Ben has now?

   A. $15 + 7 = t$

   B. $15 - 6 + 7 = t$

   C. $15 + 6 - 7 = t$

   D. $15 \div 6 = t$

6. Pang weeded gardens for 2 hours on Friday. He wants to weed gardens for a total of 5 hours on Friday and Saturday. He wrote the following equation to describe the total number of hours he wants to weed gardens on Friday and Saturday: $2 + h = 5$.

   The variable h represents the number of hours Pang will weed gardens on Saturday. Which situation does this equation describe?

   A. Pang weeded gardens for 2 hours on Friday. He wasn't sure how many hours he would weed gardens on Saturday. He wants to weed gardens for a total of 5 hours on Friday and Saturday.

   B. Pang weeded gardens for 2 hours on Friday. He weeded gardens for 5 hours on Saturday. He wasn't sure how many hours he would weed gardens on both Friday and Saturday.

   C. Pang wasn't sure how many hours he would weed gardens on Friday. He wasn't sure how many hours he would weed gardens on Saturday. He wants to weed gardens for a total of 5 hours on Friday and Saturday.

   D. Pang wasn't sure how many hours he would weed gardens on Friday. He weeded gardens for 5 hours on Saturday. He wants to weed gardens for a total of 5 hours on Friday and Saturday.

TRY IT

7. A farmer wants to plant a total of 80 stalks of corn. He plants 8 cornstalks in each row. He wrote the following equation to describe the number of rows of cornstalks he will plant: $80 = 8r$.

   The variable r represents the number of rows the farmer wants to plant. Which situation does this equation describe?

   A. A farmer wants to plant a total of 80 stalks of corn. He isn't sure how many rows of cornstalks he will plant. He isn't sure how many cornstalks he will plant in each row.

   B. A farmer wants to plant a total of 80 stalks of corn. He plants 72 rows of cornstalks. He isn't sure how many cornstalks he will plant in each row.

   C. A farmer wants to plant a total of 80 stalks of corn. He plants 8 cornstalks in each row. He isn't sure how many rows of cornstalks he will plant.

   D. A farmer wants to plant a total of 80 stalks of corn. He plants 8 cornstalks in each row. He will plant 8 rows of cornstalks.

8. April read 5 newspaper articles and 3 magazine articles every week. She wrote the following equation to represent the number of articles she read in a week: $r = 3 + 5$. The variable r represents the total number of articles April reads every week.

   Now let the variable r represent the total number of articles April reads in 6 weeks. Which equation would represent the total number of articles April would read in 6 weeks?

   A. $r = 6 + (3 + 5)$ B. $r = 3 + (6 \cdot 5)$ C. $r = (6 \cdot 3) + 5$ D. $r = 6 \cdot (3 + 5)$

9. Claudia bought some apples. She gave away 16 of them. She could represent the total number of apples she has left with the expression $a - 16$, where the variable a represents the total number of apples Claudia first bought.

   Claudia then gave away another 5 apples. Which expression represents the number of apples that Claudia has now?

   A. $16 - 5$ B. $a - 5$ C. $a - 16$ D. $a - 21$

10. Benny spends $3 a day on bus fare. He can represent the total amount he spends riding the bus with the expression $3b$, where b represents the number of days Benny rides the bus.

    The bus company is thinking of increasing the fares by $1 a day. Which expression would represent the amount Benny would spend at the new rate?

    A. $4b$ B. $12b$ C. 4×3 D. 1×3

TRY IT

11. Zoe sends letters to her pen pal by mail. She spends 42¢ on a stamp and 55¢ on an envelope. She wrote this equation to represent the total cost for sending a letter to her pen pal: $c = 42 + 55$. The variable c represents the total cost for sending a letter.

Zoe writes to her pen pal 8 times a year. Now let the variable c represent the total cost of sending her pen pals letters. Which equation would represent the total cost of sending her pen pal letters for a year?

A. $c = 8 + (42 + 55)$

B. $c = 42 + (8 \cdot 55)$

C. $c = 8 \cdot (42 + 55)$

D. $c = (8 \cdot 42) + 55$

12. Veronica had some cherries to give to 3 friends. She could represent the total number of cherries each friend would get with the expression $g \div 3$, where the variable g represents the total number of cherries Veronica has.

Veronica is thinking about giving cherries to 2 additional friends. Which expression represents the number of cherries each friend would now get?

A. $g \div 1$

B. $g \div 2$

C. $g \div 5$

D. $g \div 6$

13. Ms. Tania is planning the seating arrangements for her concert. She is dividing the seats equally into 6 rows. She could represent the total number of seats in each row with the expression $s \div 6$, where the variable s represents the total number of seats.

Ms. Tania is thinking about dividing all of the seats into 2 fewer rows than the original plan. Which expression would represent the number of seats in each row now?

A. $s \div 4$

B. $s \div 8$

C. $s \div 12$

D. $s \div 36$

14. John is planning the seating arrangements for the music show. He is dividing the total number of seats equally into 8 rows. He could represent the total number of seats in each row with the expression $t \div 8$, where the variable t represents the total number of seats.

John is thinking of dividing the seats into 2 more rows than the original plan. Which expression represents the total number of seats in each row now?

A. $t \div 6$

B. $t \div 10$

C. $t \div 16$

D. $8 + 2$

TRY IT

Expression and Equation Problems (C)

Write Story Problems

Worked Examples

You can write story problems about expressions and equations.

PROBLEM 1 There were an unknown number of people on a city bus. At the next stop, 8 people got off the bus.

This expression, with n representing the unknown number of people originally on the bus, can be written about the story problem:

$$n - 8$$

Write another story problem about this expression.

SOLUTION Figure out what the expression represents. The variable n represents an unknown number. Subtraction is the operation used, and 8 is subtracted from an unknown number.

ANSWER Some number of bicycles were parked outside a bike rental shop. Riders came out from the shop and rode away on 8 bicycles.

PROBLEM 2 There are 72 cars in a parking lot. Each row has an equal number of cars. There are 9 rows of cars. How many cars are in each row?

This equation, with t representing the unknown number of cars in each row, can be written about the story problem:

$$72 \div t = 9$$

Write another story problem about this equation.

SOLUTION Figure out what the equation means. It starts with 72. The variable t is an unknown number that divides 72. The quotient is 9.

ANSWER There were 72 clean plates in the restaurant kitchen. The plates were stacked equally in 9 stacks. How many plates were in each stack?

PROBLEM 3 Write a story problem for this equation:

$$4 \cdot m = 36$$

SOLUTION Figure out what the equation means. The variable m represents an unknown number. When it is multiplied by 4, the product is 36.

ANSWER Mark, Maria, Annie, and Jake each brought the same number of sandwiches to a picnic. The 4 friends brought a total of 36 sandwiches to the picnic. How many sandwiches did each person bring?

LEARN

Write a story problem for each expression or equation.

1. $6 + p$

2. $2a$

3. $b \div 4$

4. $f = 3 + 5$

5. $m - 4 = 6$

6. $18 = 6h$

Worked Examples

When a story problem changes, you can write a changed expression or a changed equation.

PROBLEM 1 Andrea rode the bus for a number of miles. She then walked for 1.5 miles. She could represent the miles she traveled by the expression $b + 1.5$. The variable b represents the number of miles Andrea rode on the bus.

She then rode in a taxi for twice as many miles as she rode on the bus and walked. Which expression represents the total number of miles she traveled by taxi?

In the new expression, let the variable b represent the original number of miles Andrea rode in a bus.

SOLUTION Start with the expression from the original problem. Figure out how to represent "twice as many" from the changed story problem. For "twice as many," multiply by 2.

ANSWER $2 \cdot (b + 1.5)$

PROBLEM 2 Chip hiked on a lakeside trail for 3 miles. He then hiked up a mountain trail for 2 miles. He could represent the total miles he hiked with the variable m in the equation $3 + 2 = m$.

What equation would represent the miles he hiked if he then hiked down the mountain trail for 2 miles?

In the new equation, let the variable m represent the total miles hiked on the trail and up and down the mountain.

SOLUTION Start with the equation from the original problem. Figure out how to represent an additional 2 miles from the changed story problem. For an additional 2 miles, add 2.

ANSWER $3 + 2 + 2 = m$

LEARN

Write a changed expression or changed equation.

7. Marty had 7 books checked out from the library. He returned 3 of the books. He could represent the books he still had with the variable p in the equation $7 - 3 = p$. If he then checked out 6 more books, what equation would represent how many books he had? In the new equation, let the variable p represent the total number of books Marty had after he checked out 6 more books.

8. Annette planted 20 sunflower seeds and some watermelon seeds. She could represent the number of seeds she planted with the expression $20 + w$, where w represents the number of watermelon seeds Annette planted . If Annette planted 4 times as many of the same seeds the next day, what expression would represent the number of seeds she planted on that day? In the new expression, let the variable w represent the number of watermelon seeds Annette originally planted.

9. On Monday, Wendi collected 28 grass samples for a science project. The next day she collected 8 more grass samples. She could represent the number of grass samples she collected with the variable g in the equation $28 + 8 = g$. If she then discarded 4 grass samples, what equation would represent the number of grass samples she had? In the new equation, let the variable g represent the total number of grass samples Wendi had after she discarded 4 samples.

LEARN

Quadrants in the Coordinate Plane

Complete Shapes with Coordinates

Worked Examples

You can figure out where to place a point on the coordinate plane to complete a given shape.

PROBLEM Tom's job is to plan where the four food booths at an upcoming town festival will be located. He wants the booths to be in the four corners of a square. He is using a coordinate plane to plan the location of the booths.

Here are the locations for three of the four food booths on Tom's coordinate plane:

- point A ($^+3$, $^+6$)
- point B ($^-3$, $^+6$)
- point C ($^+3$, 0)

Where will Tom locate the fourth booth, point D, to form a square on the coordinate plane?

SOLUTION

1. On the coordinate plane, locate points A, B, and C. Label each point with the point name and its ordered pair.

2. Connect the three points. Note that points A and B are 6 units apart. Note that points A and C are 6 units apart.

3. Note that point A is reflected across the y-axis to make point B.

4. Figure out the coordinates of the ordered pair for point D. Count from the origin. On the x-axis, count 3 units left from the origin. On the y-axis, count zero units up from the origin. The ordered pair is ($^-3$, 0).

5. Connect the four points with a ruler to make a square.

L E A R N

ANSWER Tom will locate the fourth booth at point D (⁻3, 0).

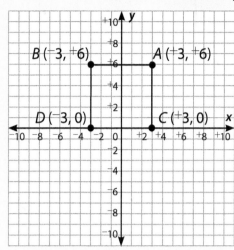

Locate and plot ordered pairs on the coordinate plane to solve.

1. Betty is planning a city vacation with her family. The family members have specific places they want to see in the city. Betty is using a coordinate plane to decide the best way for family members to visit the following sites:

   • Her sister wants to see the City Zoo at point C (⁻6, ⁻4).
   • Her dad wants to see the Jazz Museum at point J (⁻4, ⁺3).
   • Her mom wants to see the Waterfront Art Gallery at point W (⁺6, ⁺3).

   Betty wants to visit the History Museum. The location of the History Museum and the locations of the other sites make a parallelogram.

   • Name the ordered pair that describes the location of the History Museum.
   • Mark the point on a coordinate plane.
   • Label the point with its ordered pair and the letter H.
   • Connect the four points with a ruler to make a parallelogram.

LEARN

Quadrants in the Coordinate Plane

Practice with Coordinates

Choose the answer.

1. Which point on the graph shows a coordinate of ($^-$3, $^+$8)?

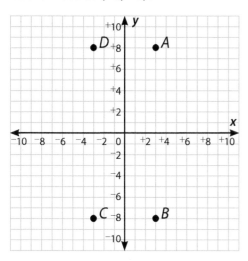

A. *A*

B. *B*

C. *C*

D. *D*

2. Which point on the graph shows a coordinate of ($^+$2, $^+$6)?

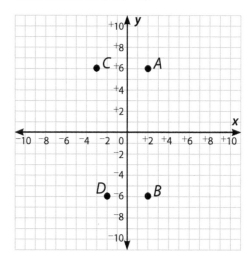

A. *A*

B. *B*

C. *C*

D. *D*

3. Which point on the graph shows a coordinate of ($^-$3, $^-$4)?

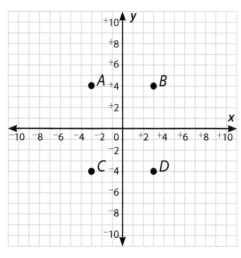

A. *A*

B. *B*

C. *C*

D. *D*

4. Which point on the graph shows a coordinate of ($^+$4, $^-$2)?

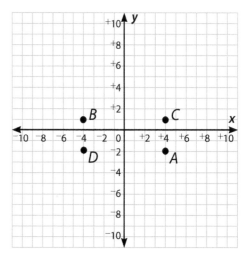

A. *A*

B. *B*

C. *C*

D. *D*

TRY IT

5. Which point on the graph shows a coordinate of ($^+$4, $^+$2)?

A. *A*

B. *B*

C. *C*

D. *D*

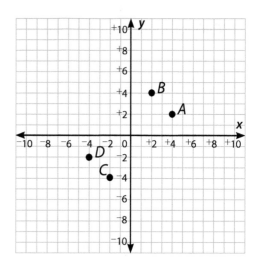

6. Which graph shows a point with a coordinate of ($^-$5, $^-$8)?

A.

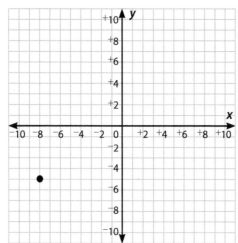

B.

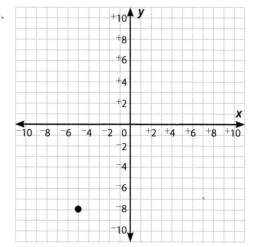

C.

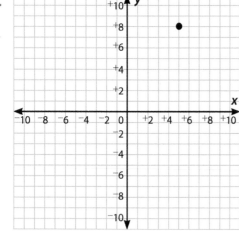

D.

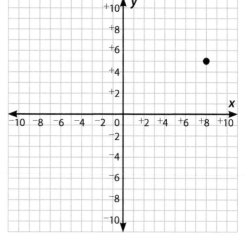

TRY IT

7. Which ordered pair is graphed?

A. $(^-5, ^+4)$

B. $(^+5, ^-4)$

C. $(^+4, ^-5)$

D. $(^-4, ^+5)$

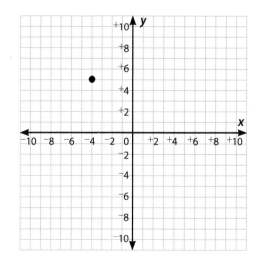

Solve.

8. Plot the following points with a dot and label each point with the ordered pair and letter.

$A (^+2, ^+3)$

$B (^-10, ^-4)$

$C (^+9, ^-5)$

$D (0, ^+3)$

$E (^-6, ^+8)$

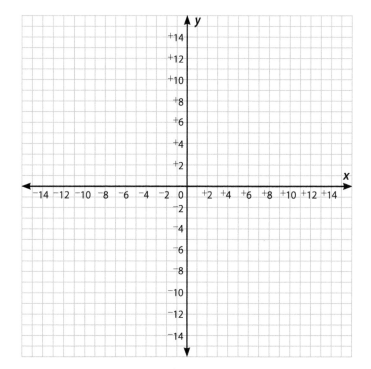

TRY IT

Ordered Pairs

Interpret Coordinates on a Graph

Worked Examples

You can describe what ordered pairs mean. You can explain what a graph means.

PROBLEM Stephen decided to collect 6 pieces of recyclable items every week. He wants to make a graph so he can predict the total amount of recyclable items he will pick up after 4 weeks. Create a graph with the following points to show how much he will pick up. Then interpret the points on the graph.

- W (1, 6)
- X (2, 12)
- Y (3, 18)
- Z (4, 24)

SOLUTION

1 Plot each point on a coordinate grid.

2 Interpret the graph:
- Explain what each ordered pair means.
- Explain whether or not a line should connect the points.
- Explain whether any of the ordered pairs can have a number less than or equal to 0 as a coordinate.
- Explain how seeing the graph makes it easier to understand what is happening in the story problem.

ANSWER

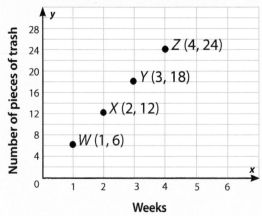

Stephen's Recycling Goals

Interpretation of the graph:

- *W* (1, 6) means that in the first week, Stephen picked up a total of 6 recyclable items.

  X (2, 12) means that in the second week, he picked up a total of 12 recyclable items.

  Y (3, 18) means that in the third week, he picked up a total of 18 recyclable items.

  Z (4, 24) means that in the fourth week, he picked up a total of 24 recyclable items.

- A line should not connect the points. It does not make sense in the problem to talk about the number of recycled items Stephen collects in $1\frac{1}{2}$ or $2\frac{1}{2}$ weeks.

- None of the ordered pairs should have a number less than or equal to 0 as a coordinate because 0 or fewer weeks and 0 or fewer recyclable items are not possible in this problem.

- It helps to see that as the number of weeks increases, the number of recyclable items increases.

Plot the points on a Quadrant I Coordinate Grid.

1. Paul collects baseball cards. Each pack has five cards. Paul decides to make a graph so that he can keep track of how many cards he has. Plot the following points and ordered pairs with their labels:

   - *A* (0, 0)
   - *B* (1, 5)
   - *C* (2, 10)
   - *D* (3, 15)

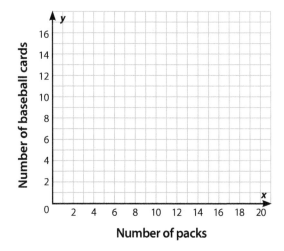

Number of Packs and Baseball Cards

Number of baseball cards

Number of packs

LEARN

Refer to the story problem and the points, ordered pairs, and labels you plotted in Problem 1 to answer the following questions.

2. What does the ordered pair (0, 0) mean?

3. What does the ordered pair (1, 5) mean?

4. What does the ordered pair (2, 10) mean?

5. What does the ordered pair (3, 15) mean?

6. Can there be a negative number of baseball card packs?

7. Can there be a negative number of baseball cards?

8. What happens to the number of baseball cards as the number of packs increase?

9. What happens to the graph as the number of packs increases and the number of cards increases?

10. Does it make sense to connect the points in the graph with a line? Why?

11. How does seeing the graph make it easier to understand what is happening in the situation?

Ordered Pairs

Practice to Understand Coordinates

Plot the points on a Quadrant I Coordinate Grid.

1. Tim's family went on vacation to Yellowstone National Park. When they left, they had 15 gallons of gas. After 1 hour, they had 12 gallons of gas left. Tim made a graph of how much gas they had left after each hour so his mother could plan when she would need to stop for gas. Plot the following points, ordered pairs, and labels, and connect the points with a line:

   - A (0, 15)
   - B (1, 12)
   - C (2, 9)
   - D (3, 6)
   - E (4, 3)
   - F (5, 0)

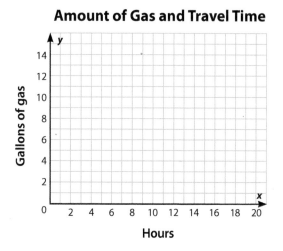

Amount of Gas and Travel Time

Refer to the story problem and the points, ordered pairs, and labels you plotted in Problem 1 to answer the following questions.

2. What does the ordered pair (0, 15) mean?

3. What does the ordered pair (1, 12) mean?

4. What does the ordered pair (2, 9) mean?

5. What does the ordered pair (3, 6) mean?

6. What does the ordered pair (4, 3) mean?

7. What does the ordered pair (5, 0) mean?

8. What happens to the hours as the gallons of gas decrease?

TRY IT

Choose the answer.

9. Ben's graph shows that the total number of medals won by Team USA on day 3 was 8. How many medals were won by day 5?

   A. 2

   B. 5

   C. 11

   D. 15

Team USA Medals Won

10. Frankie kept track of the goals scored by his soccer team. Frankie's graph shows that after 2 games his team had scored 5 goals. How many games did it take to score 9 goals?

    A. 3

    B. 6

    C. 9

    D. 13

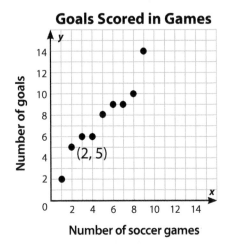

Goals Scored in Games

11. Patrice's graph shows that the total rainfall after 3 hours was 5 cm. How much rain fell from the second hour to the sixth hour?

    A. 3 cm

    B. 4 cm

    C. 6 cm

    D. 7 cm

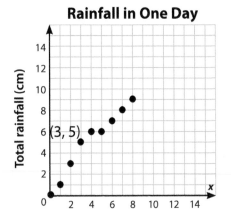

Rainfall in One Day

T R Y   I T

Graph or Write an Equation (A)

Equations and Function Tables

Worked Examples

You can use the equation for a function table to complete the table, just as you can use the rule for an input-output table to complete the table.

PROBLEM Explain what a function and a function table are. Complete a function table.

SOLUTION Below are an input-output table and a function table. By comparing the two tables, you can learn what a function table is.

- Both tables have an input column on the left. In function tables, the input column is named for a variable, such as x below.

- Both tables have an output column on the right. In function tables, the output column is named for a variable, such as y below.

- Both tables have a rule at the top, but in function tables, the rule is written as an equation and is called the function rule.

- In a function table, when you need to find a value, substitute the known value of either variable (whichever one you know) into the equation to get the value of the other variable. In an input-output table, use the rule and the known input or output to get the answer.

Input-Output Table Rule: Add 5		Function Table $y = x + 5$	
Input	Output	x	y
5	10	5	10
6	11	6	11
7	?	7	?
?	13	?	13
9	14	9	14
10	?	10	?

L E A R N

ANSWER A function is an equation that you can use to find the value of variables. In a function, put the value of a variable, such as x, into the equation. Then solve for the other variable, such as y. A function table is a table that lists input values and output values for a function rule.

To complete this table, substitute the values for x or y into the function to solve for the unknown values.

$y = x + 5$	
x	**y**
5	10
6	11
7	12
8	13
9	14
10	15

Complete the function table.

1.

$y = 2x$	
x	**y**
3	?
4	?
5	?
6	?
7	?
8	?
9	?
10	?
11	?
12	?

2.

$y = x - 2$	
x	**y**
2	?
3	?
4	?
5	?
6	?
7	?
8	?
9	?
10	?
11	?

LEARN

3.

y = x + 4	
x	**y**
10	?
11	?
12	?
?	?
14	18
?	?
16	?
17	?

4.

y = 3x	
x	**y**
1	?
2	?
3	?
?	15
8	?
?	30
12	?

L E A R N

Graph or Write an Equation (A)

Find Equations for Function Tables

Worked Examples

You can identify the equation that matches the x-values and y-values in a function table.

PROBLEM 1 Which of these two equations matches the values in the function table?

$y = x + 2$ or $y = 3x$

SOLUTION

?	
x	y
1	3
2	6
3	9

1 Substitute the x- and y-values into each equation, starting with the values in the first row.

2 Start with $y = x + 2$. Substitute 1 for x and 3 for y in that equation. Then substitute 1 for x and 3 for y in $y = 3x$.

The first and second equations are true when the values of 1 and 3 from the function table are substituted for x and y.

$y = x + 2$	
x	y
1	3

It is true that
$3 = 1 + 2$.

$y = 3x$	
x	y
1	3

It is true that
$3 = 3(1)$.

3 Substitute the values in the second row into each equation.

Only the equation $y = 3x$ is true when 2 and 6 are substituted for x and y.

$y = x + 2$	
x	y
1	3
2	6

It is **not** true that
$6 = 2 + 2$.

$y = 3x$	
x	y
1	3
2	6

It is true that
$6 = 3(2)$.

4 Check the rest of the values in the function table to make sure the equation is true for those values.

$9 = 3(3)$, so $y = 3x$ is true for all values in the function table.

LEARN

ANSWER The equation $y = 3x$ matches the values in the function table.

$y = 3x$	
x	**y**
1	3
2	6
3	9

PROBLEM 2 Which equation matches the function table?

SOLUTION

1 Look carefully at all the x- and y-values in the function table.

2 Note that each y-value is greater than the x-value on the same row. That fact helps you know which operation is used in the function. Because the y-value is greater than the x-value in each row, the equation that matches the function table must use either addition or multiplication.

3 Note that the y-value increases by 1 in all rows of the function table. Because it increases by 1, "+ 1" might be in the equation.

4 Try $y = x + 1$ as the equation that matches the function table. When you substitute 1 for x and 2 for y, the equation is true. Substitute the rest of the values into the equation.

5 When you substitute the values in each row of the function table in the equation $y = x + 1$, find that the following equations are true:

$2 = 1 + 1$	$3 = 2 + 1$	$4 = 3 + 1$
$5 = 4 + 1$	$6 = 5 + 1$	$7 = 6 + 1$

ANSWER The equation that matches the function table is $y = x + 1$.

?	
x	**y**
1	2
2	3
3	4
4	5
5	6
6	7

$y = x + 1$	
x	**y**
1	2
2	3
3	4
4	5
5	6
6	7

LEARN

Choose the equation for the function table.

1.

?	
x	y
0	4
1	5
2	6
3	7
4	8
5	9
6	10

A. $y = x + 4$

B. $y = 2x$

2.

?	
x	y
0	0
1	1
2	2
3	3
4	4
5	5
6	6

A. $y = x - 2$

B. $y = x$

Write the equation that matches the function table.

3.

?	
x	y
1	0
2	1
3	2
4	3
5	4
6	5

LEARN

Graph or Write an Equation (B)

Find an Equation Used to Make a Graph

Worked Examples

You can use the coordinates of points on the graph of a line to complete a function table. You can use the function table to find the linear equation for the graph.

PROBLEM Use the graph to complete the function table. Find the equation that was used to create the graph.

Linear Function

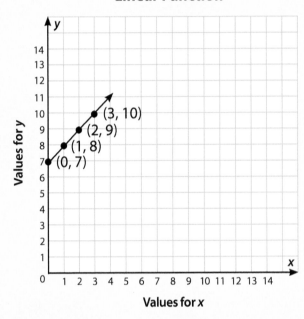

?	
x	**y**
?	?
?	?
?	?
?	?

SOLUTION

1 Use the ordered pairs from the graph to complete the blank function table.

- Ordered pair (0, 7) has 0 for the x-coordinate and 7 for the y-coordinate. Write 0 in the first row of the table in the x column. Write 7 in the first row in the y column.

- Ordered pair (1, 8) has 1 for the x-coordinate and 8 for the y-coordinate. Write 1 in the second row of the table in the x column. Write 8 in that y column.

L E A R N

- Ordered pair (2, 9) has 2 for the *x*-coordinate and 9 for the *y*-coordinate. Write 2 in the third row of the table in the *x* column. Write 9 in that *y* column.
- Ordered pair (3, 10) has 3 for the *x*-coordinate and 10 for the *y*-coordinate. Write 3 in the fourth row of the table in the *x* column. Write 10 in that *y* column.

2 Figure out the pattern of the *x*- and *y*-values in the function table.

- Each ordered pair has a *y*-value that is 7 more than the *x*-value. Because the *y*-values are greater than the *x*-values, consider using addition or multiplication of the *x*-values.
- Using information shown in the function table, see if $y = x + 7$ would work as the equation. Substitute each *x*- and *y*-value into $y = x + 7$.
- The equation is true for all the *x*- and *y*-values in the function table.

ANSWER The equation $y = x + 7$ was used to create the graph.

$y = x + 7$	
x	y
0	7
1	8
2	9
3	10

Use the graph to complete the function table.
Write the equation for the graph.

1.   **Linear Function**

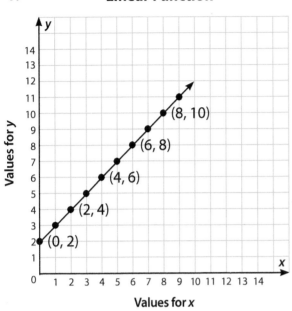

?	
?	?
?	?
?	?
?	?
?	?
?	?
?	?
?	?
?	?
?	?
?	?
?	?

2.   **Linear Function**

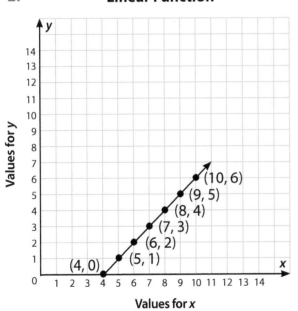

?	
?	?
?	?
?	?
?	?
?	?
?	?
?	?

LEARN

Graph or Write an Equation (B)

Practice Function Tables and Graphs

Use the graph to complete a function table.
Write the equation for the graph.

1.
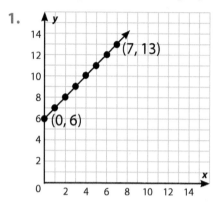

?	
x	**y**
?	?
?	?
?	?
?	?
?	?
?	?
?	?
?	?

Choose the graph that matches the equation.

2. $y = x + 2$

A.
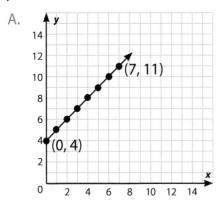
(7, 11)
(0, 4)

B.
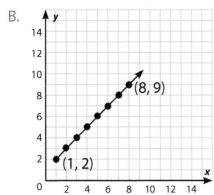
(8, 9)
(1, 2)

C.
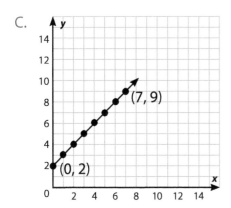
(7, 9)
(0, 2)

3. $y = x + 4$

A.
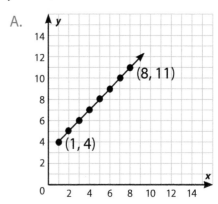
(8, 11)
(1, 4)

B.
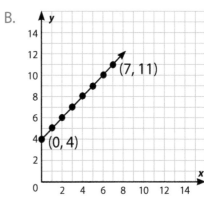
(7, 11)
(0, 4)

C.
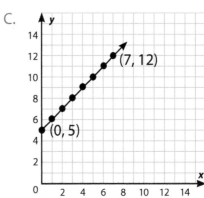
(7, 12)
(0, 5)

TRY IT

4. $y = x + 5$

A.

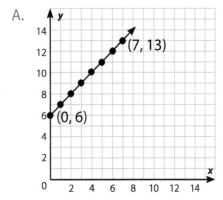

(7, 13)

(0, 6)

B.

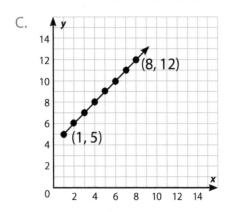

(7, 12)

(0, 5)

C.

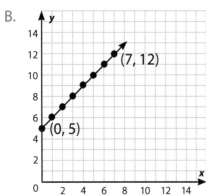

(8, 12)

(1, 5)

5. $y = x + 1$

A.

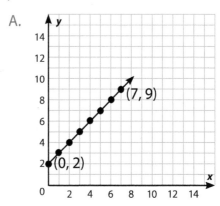

(7, 9)

(0, 2)

B.

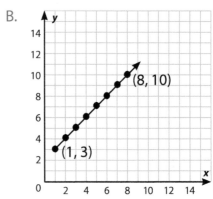

(8, 10)

(1, 3)

C.

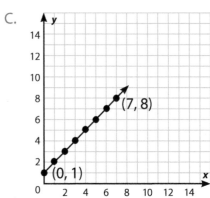

(7, 8)

(0, 1)

TRY IT

6. $y = 2x$

A.

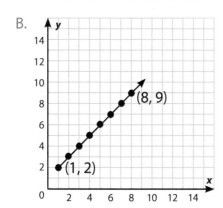

B.

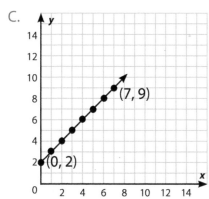

C.

7. $y = 4x$

A.

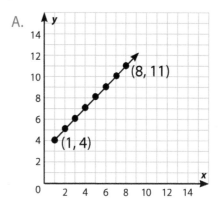

B.

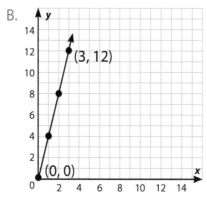

C.

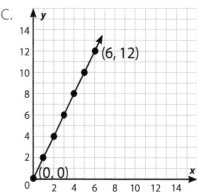

TRY IT

Choose the equation that could have been used to create the graph.

8.

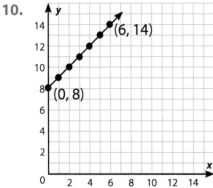

A. $y = x + 3$ B. $y = 3x$

C. $y = x + 0$ D. $y = x + 2$

9.

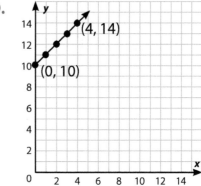

A. $y = 10x$ B. $y = x + 10$

C. $y = x + 0$ D. $y = x + 8$

10.

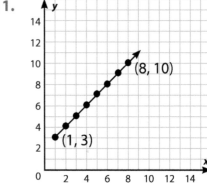

A. $y = x + 8$ B. $y = x + 1$

C. $y = 8x$ D. $y = x + 0$

11.

A. $y = x + 3$ B. $y = 2x$

C. $y = x + 0$ D. $y = x + 2$

Graph or Write an Equation (C)

Graph Equations About Animals

Worked Examples

You can create a function table and a graph to show data from a story problem about an animal.

PROBLEM A tortoise walked 5 meters in 1 minute. How many meters would the tortoise walk in 2 minutes? In 3 minutes? In 4 minutes? In 5 minutes?

Create a function table with the data. Plot the data on a graph.

SOLUTION

1 Decide what variables will represent the data. Use *m* for the number of minutes. Use *r* for the number of meters the tortoise walks. In the function table, put *m* at the top of the left-hand column and *r* at the top of the right-hand column.

2 Fill in the values for the number of minutes (*m*) in the function table. The *m* column will show 1, 2, 3, 4, and 5.

3 The number of meters (*r*) the tortoise walked in 1 minute was 5. So the number of meters the tortoise walks in 2 minutes would be 5×2. The product is 10, so a 10 is placed in row 2 in the *r* column. Find the number of meters for the rest of the *r* column by multiplying 5 by each value for *m*.

4 Find the equation that represents the relationship between *r* and *m*. The number of minutes times 5 equals the number of meters walked, so the equation that represents the values in the function table is $r = 5m$. Write the equation at the top of the function table.

5 Write a title for the coordinate grid. Label the axes and the units. The horizontal axis will represent the minutes that the tortoise walks. Label the units 1, 2, 3, 4, and 5. The vertical axis will represent the number of meters walked. Label the units 5, 10, 15, 20, 25. The vertical axis could be labeled in ones, but it would make that axis much longer than the horizontal axis.

6 Plot the points by using the values in the function table. The points are:

(1, 5)   (2, 10)   (3, 15)   (4, 20)   (5, 25)

199 GRAPH OR WRITE AN EQUATION (C)

r = 5m	
m	**r**
1	5
2	10
3	15
4	20
5	25

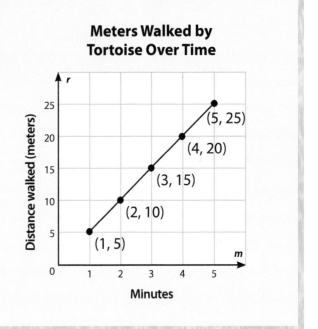

Meters Walked by Tortoise Over Time

Use the data from the story problem to create a function table.
Then plot the data on the graph.

1. A koala sleeps for more than 14 hours every day. How many hours of sleep does a koala get in 2 days? In 3 days? In 4 days? In 5 days?

?	
?	**?**
1	?
2	28
3	?
4	?
5	?

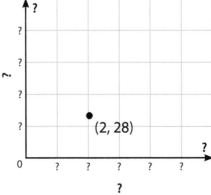

Koalas' Sleep Totals Over Time

LEARN

Graph or Write an Equation (C)

Practice with Graphs of Equations

Choose the graph that matches the story problem.

1. Carla is selling hot dogs. Each hot dog she sells comes with 4 pickles. Which graph shows the number of pickles Carla will serve if she sells *h* hot dogs?

   A.
   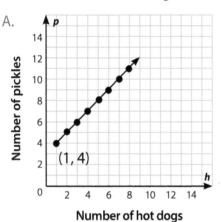
   Number of hot dogs

   B.
   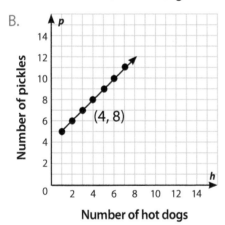
   Number of hot dogs

   C.
   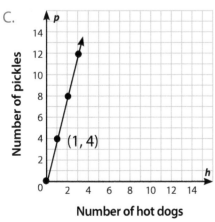
   Number of hot dogs

2. Danny is running for charity. He raises $5 for each mile he runs. Which graph shows the amount Danny will raise if he runs for *m* miles?

   A.
   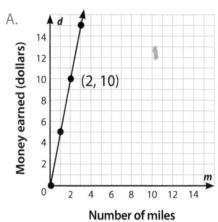
   Number of miles

   B.
   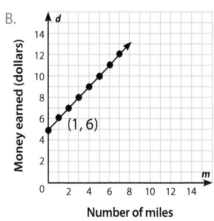
   Number of miles

   C.
   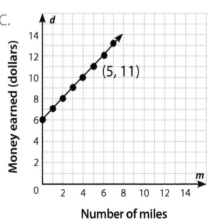
   Number of miles

TRY IT

3. At the Dandelion Café, each milkshake comes with 2 straws. Which graph shows the number of straws the café will use if it serves *m* milkshakes?

A.

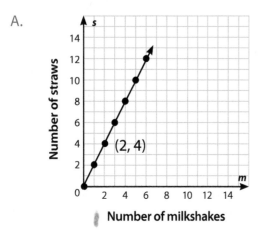

B.

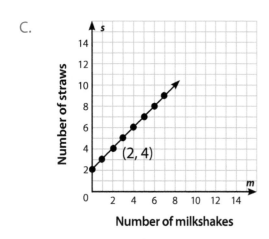

C.

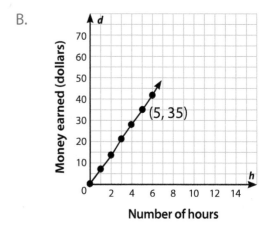

4. Tommy is paid $7 per hour for raking the leaves. Which graph shows the amount Tommy will earn if he rakes leaves for *h* hours?

A.

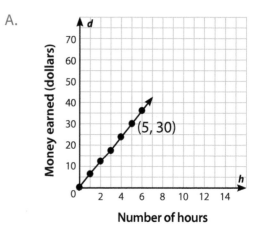

B.

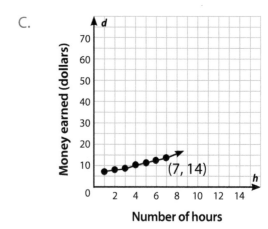

C.

GRAPH OR WRITE AN EQUATION (C)

T R Y   I T

5. Penny charges $3 for each silk flower she makes. Which graph shows the amount Penny will earn if she makes *f* silk flowers?

A.

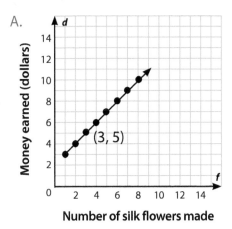

B.

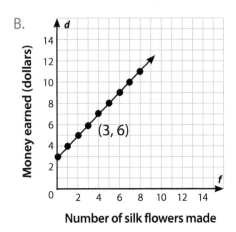

C.

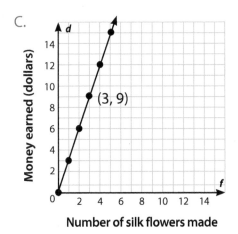

Choose the equation that matches the story problem.

6. Bobby earns $5 for every car he washes. Which equation shows the amount Bobby will earn if he washes *c* cars? (Use *t* to represent the total money earned, and *c* to represent the number of cars washed.)

   A. $t = c + 5$ B. $t = c - 5$

   C. $t = 5c$ D. $t = c \div 5$

7. Sarah is paid $7 an hour for raking the leaves. Which equation shows the amount Sarah will earn if she rakes leaves for *h* hours? (Use *t* to represent the total money earned, and *h* to represent the number of hours.)

   A. $t = 7 + h$ B. $t = 7h$

   C. $t = 7 \div h$ D. $t = 7 - h$

8. Each shirt in the store has 6 buttons. Which equation shows the number of buttons there are on *r* shirts? (Use *t* to represent the total number of buttons, and *r* to represent the number of shirts.)

   A. $t = 6r$ B. $t = 6 + r$

   C. $t = 6 - r$ D. $t = 6 \div r$

9. Tanya rides her bike 5 miles in an hour. Which equation shows the number of miles Tanya will ride in *g* hours? (Use *w* to represent the total number of miles, and *g* to represent the number of hours.)

   A. $w = 5 + g$ B. $w = 5 - g$

   C. $w = 5 \div g$ D. $w = 5g$

TRY IT

Graph or Write an Equation (D)

Graph Equations About Purchases

You can solve a story problem with decimal numbers by creating a function table, writing a two-step equation, and drawing a line graph.

PROBLEM Daniella bought 1 loaf of bread for $2.00. She also bought 4 bags of vegetables for $2.50 each. How much was her total purchase?

Also, figure out the total cost if she had purchased 5, 6, or 7 bags of vegetables.

Use the data from the story problem to complete a function table, write a two-step equation, and plot the data on the graph. Then answer the question for 4 bags of vegetables and 1 loaf of bread.

SOLUTION

1 Select the variables that will represent the data. Use v for the number of bags of vegetables Daniella selected. Use d for the amount in dollars of her purchase. In the function table, put v at the top of the left-hand column. Put d at the top of the right-hand column.

2 Figure out which variable depends on the other one. The variable d depends on the variable v because the number of dollars spent on bread and vegetables depends on the number of bags of vegetables purchased.

3 In the left column of the function table, list the values for v: 4, 5, 6, and 7.

4 Figure out what two operations the equation will have.
   - Multiplication: $2.50 must be multiplied by the number of bags of vegetables.
   - Addition: $2.00 must be added for the cost of the loaf of bread.

5 The equation is $d = 2.5v + 2$. Write the equation at the top of the function table.

6 Substitute each value for v into the equation and solve for d. Put the values for d in the right column of the function table.

7 Use the values in the function table as coordinates. Plot the points. Do not connect the points with a line. The data between the points wouldn't make sense for this story problem because Daniella cannot buy, for example, a half loaf of bread or a half bag of vegetables.

8 Give the graph a title.

$d = 2.5v + 2$	
v	d
4	12
5	14.5
6	17
7	19.5

Daniella paid $12.00 for 4 bags of vegetables and 1 loaf of bread.

Costs of Grocery Purchases

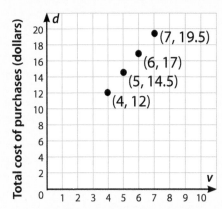

Use the data from the story problem to complete a function table, write a two-step equation, and plot the data on the graph. Then answer the question.

1. Ralph set up a lemonade stand at a soccer game. He sold jumbo cups of lemonade for $1.50 each. The total cost of supplies for the lemonade stand was $9. Ralph sold 11 jumbo cups of lemonade as soon as the stand opened. How much profit did he make?

?	
?	?
?	?
?	?
?	?
?	?
?	?
?	?
?	?
?	?

Cups of Lemonade Sold and Profit

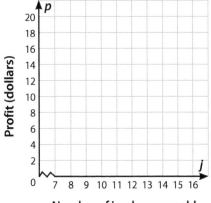

Graph or Write an Equation (D)

Graph Two-Step Equations

Choose the graph that matches the story problem.

1. Annie is saving money. Her dad said that whatever she saves, he will give her $5 more. Which graph shows the amount Annie will have if she saves *v* dollars?

   A.
   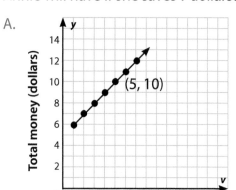
   Annie's savings (dollars)

   B.
   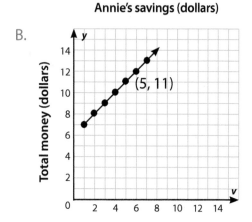
   Annie's savings (dollars)

   C.
   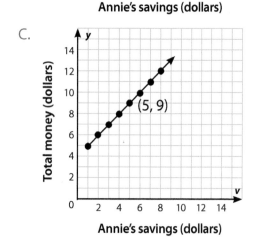
   Annie's savings (dollars)

2. Gerald is saving money. His mom said that whatever he saves, she will give him $10 more. Which graph shows the amount Gerald will have if he saves *d* dollars?

   A.
   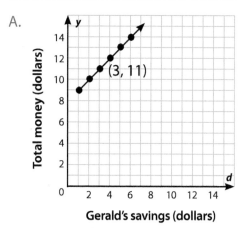
   Gerald's savings (dollars)

   B.
   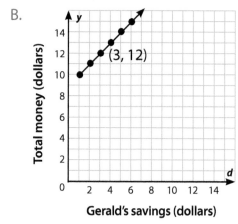
   Gerald's savings (dollars)

   C.
   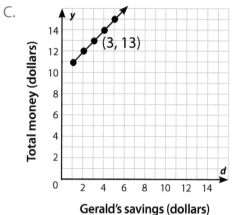
   Gerald's savings (dollars)

TRY IT

3. Taz is running for charity. He gets $1 for each mile he runs, and a fixed amount of $12. Which graph shows how much Taz will raise if he runs for *p* miles?

A.

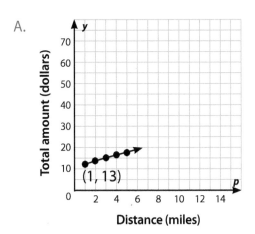

Distance (miles)

B.

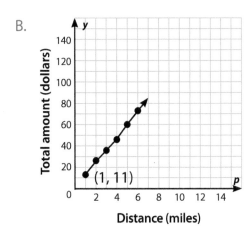

Distance (miles)

C.

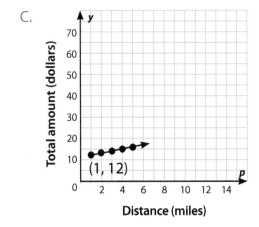

Distance (miles)

4. Raquel is collecting magazines to recycle. She gets $1 per pound and another $7 for taking the whole amount to the recycling facility. Which graph shows how many dollars Raquel will earn if she drops off *k* pounds of magazines?

A.

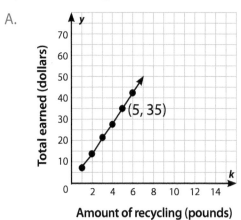

Amount of recycling (pounds)

B.

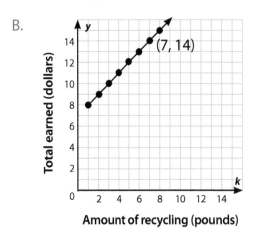

Amount of recycling (pounds)

C.

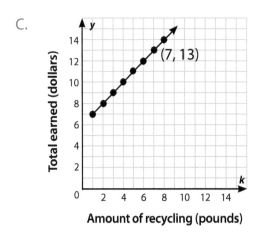

Amount of recycling (pounds)

TRY IT

Choose the equation that solves the problem.

5. Harry made 8 pennants on Monday. He plans to make a number of pennants on Tuesday. Which equation shows the total number of pennants Harry will make in two days? (Use w to represent the total number of pennants, and x to represent the number of pennants made on Tuesday.)

   A. $w = x - 8$ B. $w = x + 8$ C. $w = x \div 8$ D. $w = 8x$

6. Heidi saved \$4 last month. She plans to save more money this month. Which equation shows the total amount Heidi will save in two months? (Use m to represent the total amount of money Heidi will save, and d to represent the total amount she saves the second month.)

   A. $m = d \div 4$ B. $m = d - 4$ C. $m = d + 4$ D. $m = 4d$

7. Xavier recycled 30 pounds of paper last year. He plans to continue to recycle this year. Which equation shows how much paper Xavier will recycle in two years? (Use t to represent the total amount recycled in two years, and q to represent the amount recycled this year.)

   A. $t = 30 - q$ B. $t = 30q$ C. $t = 30 + q$ D. $t = 30 \div q$

TRY IT

Find the Perimeter of Plane Figures

Perimeter of Plane Figures

Worked Examples

You can add side lengths or use a formula to find the perimeter of regular and irregular plane figures.

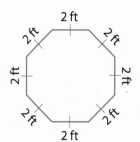

PROBLEM Workers need to replace the reflective tape around a stop sign. To know how much tape is needed, the workers must find the perimeter of the stop sign. What is the perimeter of the stop sign?

SOLUTION 1 Add the lengths of the sides.
$$2 + 2 + 2 + 2 + 2 + 2 + 2 + 2 = 16$$

SOLUTION 2 Use a formula.

1 Note that all the sides are the same length. You know they are same length because each side has one tick mark.

2 Count the sides. There are 8 sides. The shape is an octagon.

3 Write a formula to multiply the number of sides by the length of the sides.

$$P = 8s$$

The variable P stands for the perimeter. The variable s stands for the length of one side of the octagon.

4 Substitute 2 for s into the octagon perimeter formula.
$$P = 8(2)$$
$$P = 16$$

ANSWER The stop sign has a perimeter of 16 feet.

Write a formula for finding the perimeter of the plane figure. Find the perimeter.

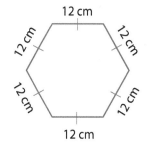

1. Mr. Kipp wants to place hexagonal tiles on the ground to make a patio. He needs to know the perimeter of each tile to determine how many tiles he will need for the patio. What is the perimeter of this hexagonal tile?

L E A R N

2. Simone wants to put ribbon around a triangular pennant she made for her favorite sports team. The pennant is an equilateral triangle with side lengths of 1.5 m. What is the perimeter of the pennant?

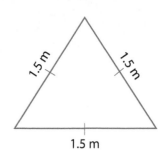

1.5 m

3. A chalk line is needed around home plate on a baseball field. To mark the plate, you need to know the perimeter. What is the perimeter of home plate?

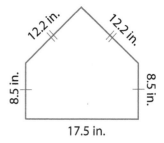

17.5 in.

4. Putt-Putt Planet miniature golf course has added a new 18th hole and needs to place wooden beams to outline the hole. To determine how much wood is needed, workers must find the perimeter of the 18th hole. What is the perimeter?

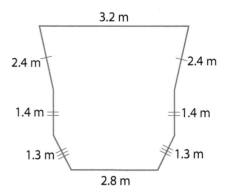

5. Thea plans to use glass square tiles in a mosaic she is building. The length of one side of each tile is 9.4 cm. What is the perimeter of each square tile?

6. Scott planted seeds for sunflowers in a garden shaped like a rectangle. He put a wooden border around the garden. The length of the garden is 8.25 ft. The width of the garden is 3.5 ft. What is the perimeter of the rectangular-shaped garden?

LEARN

Area of Parallelograms (A)

Practice Finding Parallelogram Area

Read the problem and follow the directions. Use the formula $A = bh$.
Include the unit of measurement in your answer.

1. What is the area of this parallelogram?

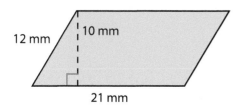

2. What is the area of a parallelogram with base 18 cm and height 6 cm?

3. Explain how to determine the area of the parallelogram. Find the area.

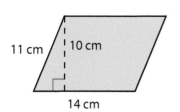

Choose the answer.

4.

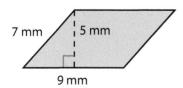

   A. 66 cm²   B. 143 cm²   C. 220 cm²   D. 260 cm²

5.

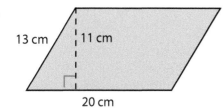

   A. 154 cm²   B. 140 cm²   C. 130 cm²   D. 50 cm²

TRY IT

6.

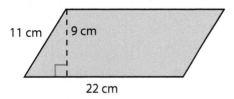

A. 198 cm²   B. 162 cm²   C. 58 cm²   D. 38 cm²

7.

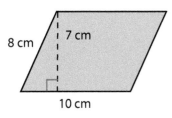

A. 25 cm²   B. 70 cm²   C. 80 cm²   D. 170 cm²

8.

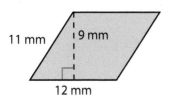

A. 108 mm²   B. 108 mm   C. 132 mm²   D. 132 mm

TRY IT

Area of Parallelograms (B)

Substitute Values to Find Area

If you know the area and either the base or height of a parallelogram, you can find the missing base or height measurement.

PROBLEM What is the length of the base of the parallelogram?

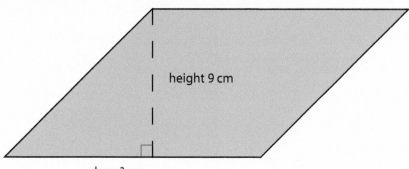

height 9 cm

base ? cm

Area = 144 cm²

SOLUTION Substitute values into the area formula $A = bh$. Substitute 144 for the area and 9 for the height. Solve by using the inverse operation on both sides of the equation. It leaves b alone on the right side of the equation.

$$A = bh$$
$$144 = b \cdot 9$$
$$144 \div 9 = b \cdot 9 \div 9$$
$$144 \div 9 = b$$
$$16 = b$$

ANSWER The length of the base of this parallelogram is 16 cm.

LOOK BACK

Check your answer.

$$A = bh$$
$$A = 16 \cdot 9$$
$$A = 144$$

The area of a parallelogram that has a base of 16 cm and a height of 9 cm has an area of 144 cm². That area matches the area given in the problem.

L E A R N

Read the problem and follow the directions. Use the formula $A = bh$.

1. The area of this parallelogram is 21.7 m². The height is 3.5 m. What is the length of the base of the parallelogram?

2. The area of this parallelogram is 51 yd². The length of the base is 8.5 yd. What is the height of the parallelogram?

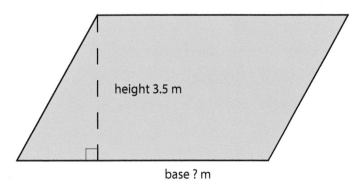

height 3.5 m

base ? m

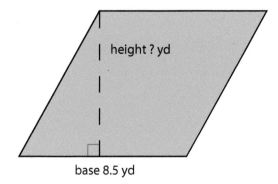

height ? yd

base 8.5 yd

Find the area. Use the formula $A = bh$. Show your work.

3.

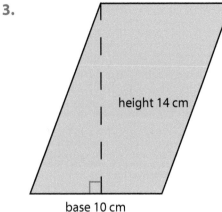

height 14 cm

base 10 cm

4.

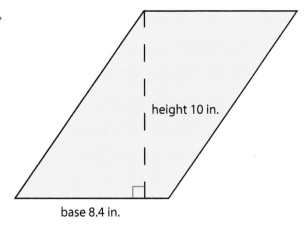

height 10 in.

base 8.4 in.

5.

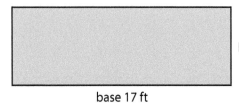

height 5.9 ft

base 17 ft

6.

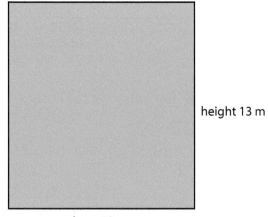

height 13 m

base 12 m

LEARN

You can find the area of a parallelogram if you know the area of a triangle formed by cutting the parallelogram diagonally in half.

PROBLEM The area of triangle *DEF* is 36 cm². What is the area of parallelogram *DEFG*?

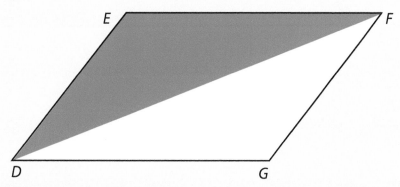

SOLUTION The area of a triangle formed by cutting a parallelogram diagonally in half is equal to half the area of the parallelogram. Multiply the area of the triangle by 2 to find the area of the parallelogram.

$$36 \cdot 2 = 72$$

ANSWER The area of parallelogram *DEFG* is 72 cm².

Find the area. Show your work.

7. The shaded triangle has an area of 105 mm². What is the area of this parallelogram?

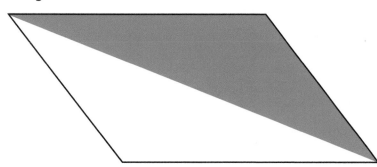

LEARN

Area of a Parallelograms (B)

Story Problems on Parallelogram Area

You can solve story problems about the area of parallelograms. You can find the area of a parallelogram when the base and height are given as measurements related to each other.

PROBLEM The height of a parallelogram-shaped tile is 5.4 cm more than the length of its base. If the base is 12 cm, what is the area of the tile in centimeters squared?

SOLUTION Use the area formula $A = bh$.

1. State the measurements you know. You know that the base is 12 cm and the height is 5.4 cm more than the base.

2. Since the height is more than the base by 5.4 cm, add 5.4 cm to the measurement of the base. Then you'll have the height measurement.
$$12 + 5.4 = 17.4$$

3. Substitute the base and height measurements into the area formula. Use order of operations to find the area.
$$A = bh$$
$$A = 12 \cdot (12 + 5.4)$$
$$A = 12 \cdot 17.4$$
$$A = 208.8$$

ANSWER The area of the tile is 208.8 cm².

Find the area. Use the formula $A = bh$. Show your work.

1. Charlene has a poster that is shaped like a parallelogram. The height of the poster is 3 times the length of its base. If the base is 18 inches, what is the area of the poster in inches squared?

2. A garden is in the shape of a parallelogram. The garden has an area of 72 m². Give 4 possible whole-number measurements for the base and height.

3. Mr. Donne is going to build a patio in the shape of a parallelogram. The base of the patio will be 13 feet. The height of the patio will be 11 feet. He needs to know the area of the patio so he can order concrete. What will the area of the patio be?

4. A park in the shape of a parallelogram had a path that crossed it diagonally, dividing it in half. A triangle bordered by the path and 2 sides of the park had an area of 225 yd². What was the area of the park?

Area of Parallelograms (B)

Solve Parallelogram Area Problems

Find the area. Use the formula $A = bh$.

1.

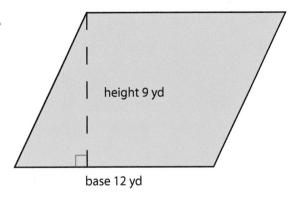

height 9 yd

base 12 yd

2.

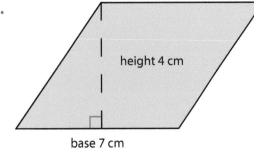

height 4 cm

base 7 cm

3.

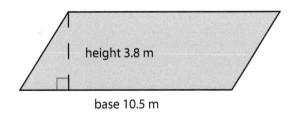

height 3.8 m

base 10.5 m

Read the problem and follow the directions.

4. What is the area of a parallelogram with a base of 110 cm and a height of 5 cm?

5. What is the area of a parallelogram with a base of 78 mm and a height of 9 mm?

6. What is the measure of the height of a parallelogram with a base of 26.4 in. and an area of 456.72 in^2?

7. Explain how you know that the area of a parallelogram with a base of 12 cm and a height of 5 cm is the same as the area of a rectangle with a base of 12 cm and a height of 5 cm.

T R Y   I T

218

Choose the answer.

8.

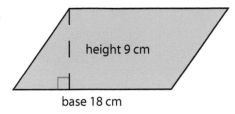

base 18 cm

A. 162 cm²   B. 99 cm²

C. 58 cm²   D. 38 cm²

9.

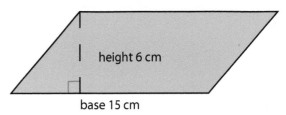

base 15 cm

A. 31 cm²   B. 45 cm²

C. 90 cm²   D. 120 cm²

T R Y   I T

Area of Parallelograms and Triangles

Read the problem and follow the directions.

1. Use the formula $A = bh$ to find the area of the rectangle.
   What is the area of the rectangle?

   Explain how to find the area of one of the right triangles.

   What is the area of the right triangle?

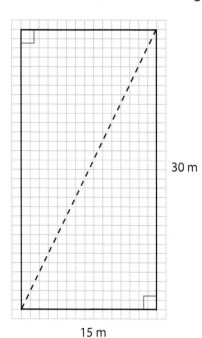
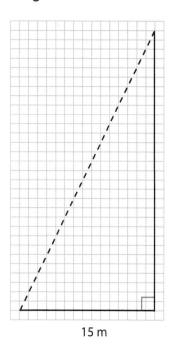
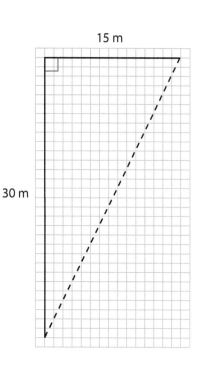

2. Use the formula $A = bh$ to find the area of the parallelogram.
   What is the area of the parallelogram?

   Explain how to find the area of one of the acute triangles.

   What is the area of the acute triangle?

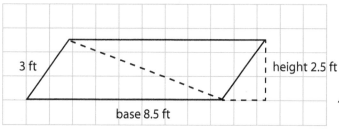
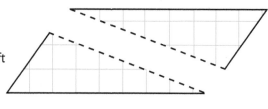

Nets, Solids, and Surface Area

Solve Surface Area Problems

Worked Examples

You can find the surface area of a rectangular prism and a cube.

PROBLEM 1 What is the surface area of this rectangular prism? Use the rectangular prism's net and an equation to find the answer.

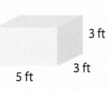

3 ft

3 ft

5 ft

3 ft

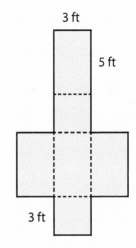

3 ft

5 ft

3 ft

SOLUTION

1 Read the measurement labels on the sides of the rectangular prism's faces. The rectangular prism has a length of 5 ft, a width of 3 ft, and a height of 3 ft.

2 Read and record the measurements of each figure on the net. Write the area of each figure as an expression of length • width. ⟶

3 Use the expressions to write an equation to find the rectangular prism's surface area.

$$\text{surface area} = (3 \cdot 5) + (3 \cdot 5) + (3 \cdot 5) + (3 \cdot 5) + (3 \cdot 3) + (3 \cdot 3)$$

$$= 4(3 \cdot 5) + 2(3 \cdot 3)$$

$$= 4(15) + 2(9)$$

$$= 60 + 18$$

$$= 78$$

3 ft

3 • 5   5 ft

3 • 3

3 • 5 | 3 • 5 | 3 • 5

3 ft | 3 • 3

ANSWER The surface area of the rectangular prism is 78 ft².

L E A R N

PROBLEM 2 What is the surface area of this rectangular prism?
Use the rectangular prism's net and an equation to find the answer.

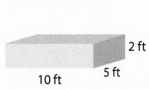

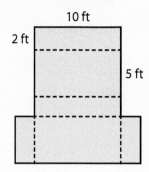

SOLUTION

1 Read the measurement labels on the sides of the rectangular prism's faces. It has sides that measure 10 ft, 5 ft, and 2 ft. Some rectangular prisms, such as this one, have sides of 3 different lengths rather than 2 different lengths. That means you'll have 3 different expressions in your equation.

2 Read and record the measurements of each figure on the net. Write the area of each figure as an expression of length • width. ⟶

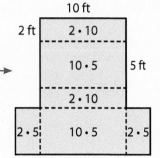

3 Use the expressions to write an equation to find the rectangular prism's surface area.

surface area $= (10 \cdot 5) + (10 \cdot 5) + (2 \cdot 10) + (2 \cdot 10) + (2 \cdot 5) + (2 \cdot 5)$

$\qquad = 2(10 \cdot 5) + 2(2 \cdot 10) + 2(2 \cdot 5)$

$\qquad = 2(50) + 2(20) + 2(10)$

$\qquad = 100 + 40 + 20$

$\qquad = 160$

ANSWER The surface area of the rectangular prism is 160 ft².

LEARN

Find the surface area. Use the net to help you.

1. rectangular prism

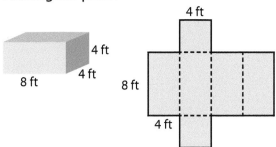

4 ft
4 ft
4 ft
8 ft
8 ft
4 ft

2. rectangular prism

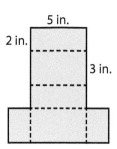

2 in.
5 in.
3 in.
5 in.
2 in.
3 in.

PROBLEM 3 What is the surface area of this cube? Use only an equation.

SOLUTION Multiply the number of congruent faces in a cube (6) by the area of each face. For the area of a face, write length • width.

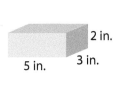

4 ft

surface area $= 6(4 • 4)$

$= 6(16)$

$= 96$

ANSWER The surface area of the cube is 96 ft².

Find the surface area. Use an equation.

3. cube

3 cm

4. cube

5 m

Write an equation to solve the problem. Include the unit of measure with the answer.

5. Mr. Sanchez wants to paint a toy box for his granddaughter. The toy box is a cube shape. Mr. Sanchez needs to know the surface area of the toy box so he can buy the correct amount of paint. What is the surface area of the toy box?

2 ft

6. Rachel wants to wrap several boxes that are rectangular prisms. She needs to find the surface area of one box to help her know how much wrapping paper to buy. What is the surface area of one box?

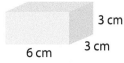

3 cm
3 cm
6 cm

L E A R N

Nets, Solids, and Surface Area

Find Surface Area

Find the surface area of the cube.

1.

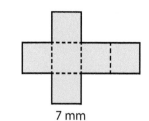

7 mm

7 mm

2.

3 cm

3 cm

3.

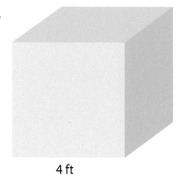

4 ft

Find the surface area of the rectangular prism.

4.

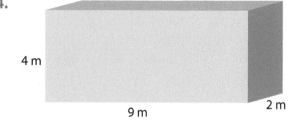

4 m

9 m

2 m

TRY IT

Choose the answer.

5.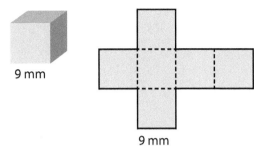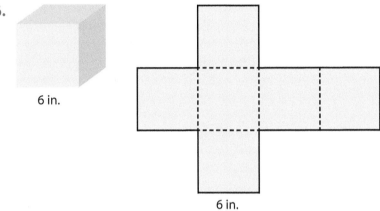

9 mm

9 mm

A. 54 mm²   B. 81 mm²   C. 486 mm²   D. 729 mm²

6.

6 in.

6 in.

A. 36 in²   B. 144 in²   C. 216 in²   D. 288 in²

7.

2 cm

5 cm   3 cm

A. 20 cm²   B. 30 cm²   C. 50 cm²   D. 62 cm²

8.

2 cm

10 cm   6 cm

A. 184 cm²   B. 120 cm²   C. 50 cm²   D. 24 cm²

T R Y   I T

Area of Irregular Shapes

Solve Area Problems

Worked Examples

You can estimate the area of an irregular shape.

PROBLEM What is the approximate area of this lake? Each square represents 1 square mile (1 mi²).

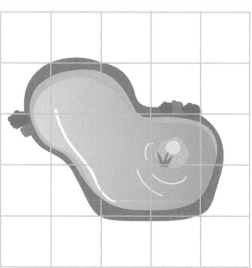

SOLUTION Follow the steps to make your estimate.

1 Look at the lake to see if it is irregular. An irregular shape has some parts that cover parts of squares on a grid. The lake has sections that cover only parts of squares, so it is irregular.

2 Count the whole squares covered by the lake and its border. The lake covers 5 whole squares on the grid.

3 Count the partial squares covered by the lake and its border. The lake covers 11 partial squares on the grid.

4 Combine the partial squares. Estimate how much of a whole square each partial square represents. Think about if each partial square fills about $\frac{1}{4}$, $\frac{1}{2}$, or $\frac{3}{4}$ of the whole square. Count the whole squares you get. You could estimate that the combined partial squares would equal about 4 whole squares.

5 Add the 5 whole squares you counted to the 4 squares made up of partial squares.

ANSWER A close approximate answer would be 9 mi². Because this shape is irregular, other approximate answers are acceptable. Approximate answers for this problem can range from 5 mi² to 16 mi².

LEARN

Solve.

1. Find the approximate area of this rug on a tile floor. Each square represents 1 ft².

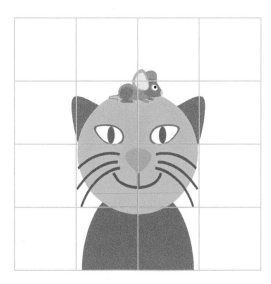

2. Tanya is raking leaves in her yard. Her yard is the irregular green shape on the grid. What is the approximate area of her yard? Each square represents 1 yd².

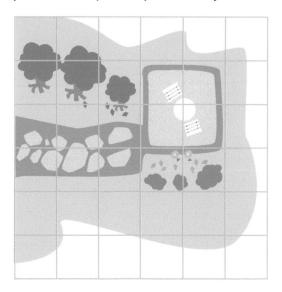

3. What is the approximate area of this swimming pool including the slide, border, and plants? Each square represents 4 ft².

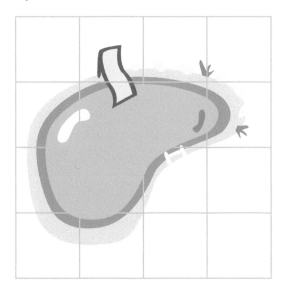

4. This drawing represents the shape of the state of Nevada. What is the approximate area of this shape? Each square represents 10,000 mi².

L E A R N

Area of Irregular Shapes

Area and Irregular Shapes

Solve.

1. What is the approximate area of this garden? Each square represents 1 ft².

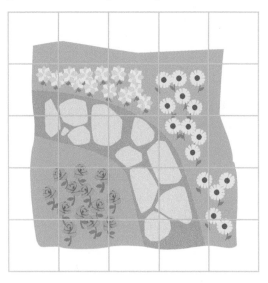

2. What is the approximate area of this pond? Each square represents 1 yd².

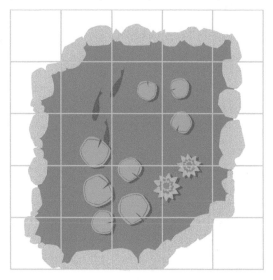

3. What is the approximate area of this backyard? Each square represents 1 yd².

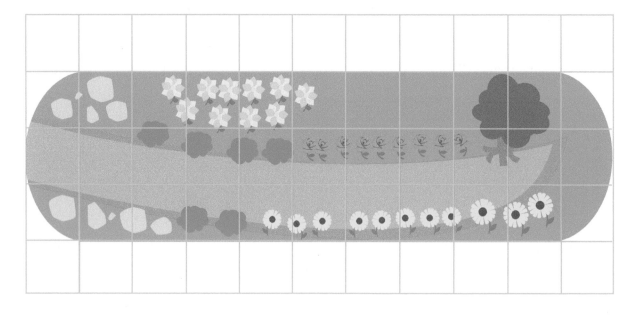

TRY IT

4. What is the approximate area of this lake? Each square represents 1 km².

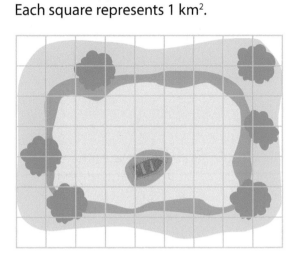

5. What is the approximate area of this tan-colored paint spill? Each square represents 1 cm².

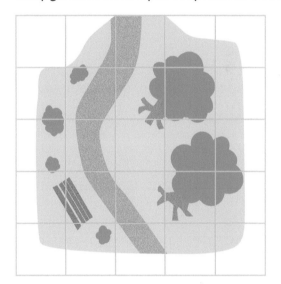

6. What is the approximate area of this kite? Each square represents 1 cm².

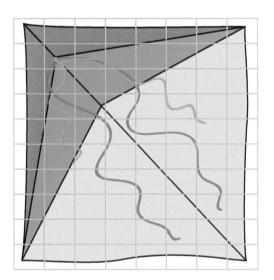

7. What is the approximate area of this campground? Each square represents 1 m².

TRY IT

Volume of Solid Figures (A)

Practice Volume of Solid Figures

Read the problem and follow the directions.

1. There are 15 centimeter cubes in each layer in this rectangular prism. Explain why the volume of this rectangular prism is 90 cm³.

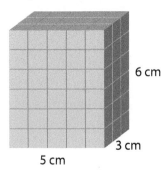

6 cm

3 cm

5 cm

2. Find the volume of the rectangular prisms by counting the cubes in each layer.

Each cube is 1 cm³.

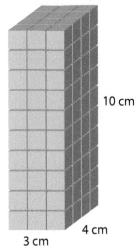

10 cm

4 cm

3 cm

TRY IT

Choose the answer.

3. Each cube is 1 cm³.

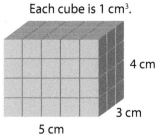

4 cm

3 cm

5 cm

A. 12 cm³   B. 15 cm³

C. 60 cm³   D. 94 cm³

4. Each cube is 1 in³.

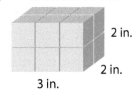

2 in.

2 in.

3 in.

A. 7 in³   B. 12 in³

C. 24 in³   D. 322 in³

5. Each cube is 1 in³.

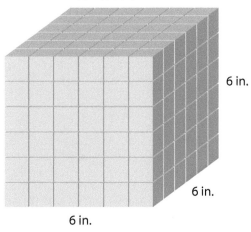

6 in.

6 in.

6 in.

A. 12 in³   B. 36 cm³

C. 72 cm³   D. 216 in³

6. Each cube is 1 in³.

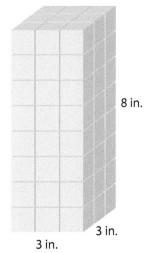

8 in.

3 in.

3 in.

A. 14 in³   B. 72 in³

C. 216 in³   D. 338 in³

TRY IT

Volume of Solid Figures (B)

Use the Volume Formula

Worked Examples

You can use the volume formula $V = lwh$ to find the volume of a rectangular prism. You can also use the volume formula to find the length, width, or height of a rectangular prism if you know the area and two of the other measurements.

PROBLEM 1 What is the volume of the cereal box?

SOLUTION Substitute the given values into the volume formula $V = lwh$.

$V = lwh$
$V = 7 \cdot 3 \cdot 10$
$V = 210$

ANSWER The volume of the cereal box is 210 in³.

Cereal

height 10 in.

12.5 ounces.

width 3 in.

length 7 in.

PROBLEM 2 The volume of this storage container is 1,400 in³. The length is 14 in. and the width is 20 in. What is the measure of the height of the storage container?

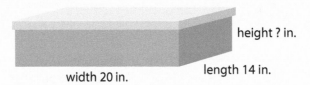

height ? in.

width 20 in.

length 14 in.

SOLUTION Substitute the given values into the volume formula $V = lwh$. Solve for the missing value.

$$V = lwh$$
$$1{,}400 = 14 \cdot 20 \cdot h$$
$$1{,}400 = 280 \cdot h$$
$$1{,}400 \div 280 = 280 \div 280 \cdot h$$
$$1{,}400 \div 280 = h$$
$$5 = h$$

ANSWER The height of the storage container is 5 in.

LEARN

Use the volume formula $V = lwh$ to solve.

1. Find the volume of this rectangular prism.

   The length is 7 inches.
   The width is 9 inches.
   The height is 4 inches.

   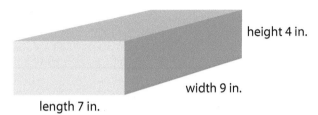

   height 4 in.

   width 9 in.

   length 7 in.

2. What is the volume of this rectangular prism?

   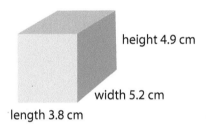

   height 4.9 cm

   width 5.2 cm

   length 3.8 cm

3. What is the length of this rectangular prism?

   volume = 252 ft³

   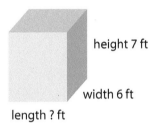

   height 7 ft

   width 6 ft

   length ? ft

4. What is the volume of this cube?

   Hint: A cube is a special kind of rectangular prism.

   length 5 m

5. What is the height of this rectangular prism?

   volume = 24 cm³

   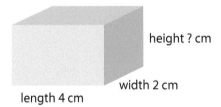

   height ? cm

   width 2 cm

   length 4 cm

LEARN

6. What is the volume of a shipping box with length 6 feet, width 12 feet, and height 13 feet?

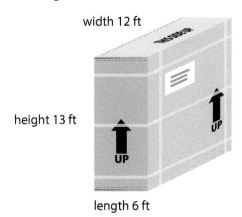

width 12 ft

height 13 ft

UP

UP

length 6 ft

7. What is the volume of a toy chest with length 3.6 feet, width 2.1 feet, and height 2.4 feet?

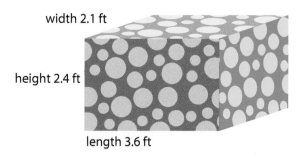

width 2.1 ft

height 2.4 ft

length 3.6 ft

8. What is the width of this rectangular prism?

volume = 72 m³

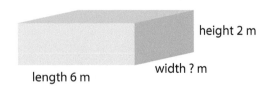

height 2 m

length 6 m

width ? m

9. What is the volume of this rectangular prism?

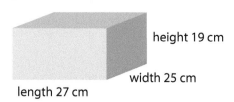

height 19 cm

width 25 cm

length 27 cm

10. What is the volume of this cube-shaped gift box?

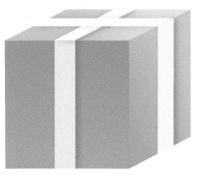

length 8 in.

Volume of Solid Figures (B)

Practice the Formula for Volume

Use the volume formula $V = lwh$ to solve.

1. Explain how to calculate the volume of this shoe box.
   What is the volume of the shoe box?

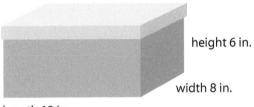

height 6 in.

width 8 in.

length 12 in.

2. What is the volume of this rectangular prism? Each cube is 1 cm³.

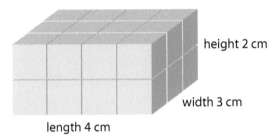

height 2 cm

width 3 cm

length 4 cm

3. The volume of a computer box is 1,904 in³. The length is 17 in. and the height is 16 in. What is the measure of the width of the box?

TRY IT

Steps to Solve Story Problems (B)

Analyze Problems and Make Steps

Worked Examples

You can select the information you need to solve a story problem. You can figure out what steps to use for solving the problem and put the steps in order.

PROBLEM Camille was studying the art of American painter Jackson Pollock. For an art lesson, she needed to write a report and paint a picture in the painter's style. She and her mother decided to go to the art supply store. Camille wrote a list that included paintbrushes, at least 4 different colors of paint, 2 sheets of poster board, and construction paper.

At the store, Camille selected the supplies. When she had finished, she and her mother were ready to purchase the following items:

- 1 package of paintbrushes: $4.99
- 2 large bottles of paint, red and blue: 3 bottles for $5.79
- 2 small bottles of paint, orange and green: $1.39 each
- 2 sheets of poster board: $2.29 each
- 1 package of white construction paper: $2.79

There is a 9% sales tax on the art supplies.

Camille and her mother decided that Camille will pay for the paint and the 2 sheets of poster board, including tax. Her mother will pay for the other items.

What steps would you follow to calculate how much Camille will pay?

SOLUTION

UNDERSTAND THE PROBLEM

Ask yourself the following questions to help you understand what the problem is asking:

Do I understand all the words in the problem? If you don't, then look them up in a dictionary or ask someone who is likely to know the meaning of the word.

What am I asked to find, explain, or show? You need to find the amount that Camille will pay.

How can I restate the problem in my own words? An example is this question: How much money will Camille owe for 4 bottles of paint and 2 sheets of poster board?

Can I sketch something to help me understand the problem? There isn't an obvious sketch that can be used to solve this problem. But in other problems, a sketch might help you.

What information do I have, what do I need, and what do I **not** need? You have some information about the cost of various art supplies to be purchased. You need more information about prices, such as the per-item price for the large bottles of paint. You need to figure out the amount of sales tax by using the given percent. You don't need the cost of the paintbrushes and construction paper or the color of the paint.

LEARN

DEVISE A PLAN

You can follow a set of steps to help you find the amount Camille will pay. A list of the steps in order can help you.

1 Figure out the cost of the 2 large paint bottles.

2 Figure out the cost of the 2 small paint bottles.

3 Figure out the cost of the 2 sheets of poster board.

4 Add those three amounts to get a total.

5 Calculate the 9% sales tax on the total.

6 Add the sales tax to the total to get the amount that Camille will pay.

CARRY OUT THE PLAN

You can go through your list to help you stay organized.

You can do Steps 1, 2, and 3 in any order. But you cannot do Steps 4, 5, and 6 in any order. You can use your reasoning skills to figure out which steps you need to do in a specific order.

1 Find the cost of the 2 large paint bottles.
- Divide the cost of 3 bottles by 3. $\$5.79 \div 3$
- Multiply the quotient by 2. $\$1.93 \cdot 2$

2 Find the cost of the 2 small paint bottles. $\$1.39 \cdot 2$

3 Find the cost of the 2 sheets of poster board. $\$2.29 \cdot 2$

4 Add the costs of the supplies.
The 2 large paint bottles cost $3.86.
The 2 small paint bottles cost $2.78.
The 2 sheets of poster board cost $4.58.
$\$3.86 + \$2.78 + \$4.58$

5 Calculate the sales tax by multiplying 0.09 by the total.
$\$11.22 \cdot 0.09$

6 Add the sales tax to the total.
$\$11.22 \cdot 0.09$ equals about $1.00.
$\$11.22 + \$1.00$

LOOK BACK

Ask yourself these questions:

Did I answer the question of how much money Camille will pay for the art supplies? Yes, the answer is the cost of her share of the supplies including sales tax.

How should I decide if the answer makes sense? Round the prices of the items and use estimation to get an estimated answer. Then compare it with the actual answer. At each step, you can round the prices to the nearest dollar and then multiply. Then add the products. Figure the tax and add it to the costs of the art supplies.

Have I forgotten anything? Look back at the problem to make sure you haven't forgotten anything. Double-check the math.

ANSWER

1 Figure out the cost of the 2 large paint bottles.

2 Figure out the cost of the 2 small paint bottles.

3 Figure out the cost of the 2 sheets of poster board.

4 Add those three amounts to get a total.

5 Calculate the 9% sales tax on the total.

6 Add the sales tax to the total to get the amount that Camille will pay.

L E A R N

Read the problem and follow the directions.

1. Answer the question about the following story problem:

   Gerard and Emily rode their bikes on a bike trail. Gerard rode for 2 hours at an average speed of 8 miles per hour. Emily rode for 3 hours at an average speed of 6 miles per hour.

   What steps would you follow to calculate the difference in the distances they rode?

2. Answer the question about the following story problem:

   Clarice had 18 containers that she needed to fill with water and carry outside. She could fill and carry 3 containers every 5 minutes. How many containers would she still need to fill after 15 minutes had passed?

   What step should you do first to solve this story problem?

3. List steps in a correct order for solving the story problem. Then solve the problem.

   Don wants to earn money so he can save to go on a trip. He offers these services to his 7 neighbors:

   - Dog walking: $2.50 per dog
   - Car washing: $4.00 per car
   - Driveway sweeping: $1.25 per driveway
   - Watering and weed pulling: $9.50 per week for each flower bed or vegetable bed

   A neighbor with 2 driveways asks him to sweep both of his driveways. A neighbor with 3 dogs asks him to walk 2 of the dogs. A neighbor with 4 cars asks him to wash 3 of the cars. A neighbor with a flower bed asks him to weed the bed for 2 weeks.

   What steps would you follow to calculate how much Don earned from these jobs?

LEARN

Break Down Multistep Problems

Simpler Parts

Worked Examples

You can determine when and how to break a story problem into simpler parts.

PROBLEM Answer the questions about this story problem:

Eduardo saved $3.00 from his allowance every week for 12 weeks. He spent $\frac{3}{4}$ of the saved amount on a baseball glove. Later, he spent $\frac{1}{3}$ of the remaining amount on a baseball book. How much money does he have left?

Should the problem be broken into simpler problems? If so, how should it be done?

SOLUTION

UNDERSTAND THE PROBLEM

To figure out if the problem should be broken into simpler parts, ask yourself these questions:

What am I asked to find, explain, or show? You are asked to find how much of Eduardo's savings of 12 weeks he has left.

How can I restate the problem in my own words? Eduardo saved a sum of money. He spent a fraction of the money. Then later he spent another fraction of the remaining money.

What information do I have, what do I need, and what do I **not** need? You know how much he saved each week for 12 weeks. You know the fractional amounts he spent on a baseball glove and a book. You know he spent the money at different times. You need to calculate how much he saved, each amount he spent, and how much he has left.

Yes, the problem requires several calculations, so it should be broken into simpler parts. To break it into simpler problems, devise a plan.

DEVISE A PLAN

To break the problem into simpler parts, make a list of the calculations you need to do.

1 Calculate how much Eduardo saved in 12 weeks.

2 Calculate how much he spent on the baseball glove.

3 Subtract that amount from his savings.

4 Calculate how much of his remaining savings he spent on the baseball book.

5 Subtract that amount from his remaining savings.

CARRY OUT THE PLAN

1 Multiply to find out how much Eduardo saved in 12 weeks.

2 Multiply the amount of money he saved by $\frac{3}{4}$ to find out how much he spent on the glove.

3 Subtract that amount from his savings.

4 Multiply the difference by $\frac{1}{3}$ to find out how much he spent on the book.

5 Subtract that amount from his remaining savings.

LOOK BACK

Ask yourself these questions:

Did I answer the question of whether to break the problem into simpler parts? Yes.

Did I answer the question of how to break the problem into simpler parts? Yes. You made a list of the calculations needed for solving the problem.

ANSWER Yes, the problem should be broken into simpler parts. The simpler parts are the calculations needed to find the final answer.

Read the problem and follow the directions.

1. What calculations could be used to solve this problem?

   A popular singer was on a concert tour. Attendance at the concerts was 7,845 for each of the first 4 performances and 6,920 for the final performance. How many people in all attended the concerts?

Choose the answer.

2. Which describes the calculations that could be used to solve this problem?

   A coin collector keeps 1,482 coins in 6 jars. Each jar contains an equal number of coins. Nine coins in each jar are gold coins. How many coins in each jar are **not** gold coins?

   A. Subtract 6 from 1,482. Then divide by 9.

   B. Add 6 to 1,482. Then divide by 9.

   C. Divide 1,482 by 6. Then subtract 9.

   D. Multiply 1,482 by 6. Then subtract 9.

L E A R N

3. Read the problem and review the data in the table. What calculations could be used to solve the following problem?

What is the cost of 8 packages of stickers?

A. Multiply $3.45 by 8.
   Subtract $2.29 from the product.

B. Multiply $3.45 by 8.
   Add $2.75 to the product.

C. Divide $5.99 by 8.

D. Multiply $3.45 by 8.

Scrapbooking Supplies	
Scrapbooks	$5.99 each
Stickers	$3.45 per package
Rubber Stamps	$2.29 each
Stencils	$2.75 each

4. Which simpler problems could be calculated to solve this problem?

Ray, Nancy, and Elaine collected a total of 982 cans of food for the canned food drive. Ray collected 178 cans. Nancy and Elaine collected an equal number of cans. How many cans did Nancy collect?

A. Find the number of cans Ray collected.
   Then find the total number of cans Ray, Nancy, and Elaine collected.

B. Find the total number of cans Ray, Nancy, and Elaine collected.
   Then find the number of cans Nancy collected.

C. Find the number of cans Nancy collected.
   Then find the total number of cans Nancy and Elaine collected.

D. Find the number of cans Nancy and Elaine collected.
   Then find the number of cans Nancy collected.

LEARN

Mathematical Reasoning Methods (A)

Choose the Best Strategy

Choose the problem-solving strategy and explanation that correctly show how to solve the problem.

1. Daniella made 1 triangle with 3 toothpicks. She discovered she could make 2 triangles if she used 5 toothpicks. If she used 7 toothpicks, she could make 3 triangles. How many toothpicks would Daniella need to make 7 triangles?

   A. **Write an equation.**
      $(1 \cdot 3) + (2 \cdot 5) + (3 \cdot 7) = ?$
      Calculate the number of toothpicks needed to make each triangle and add them all up.

   B. **Guess and test.**
      Guess 17 toothpicks for 7 triangles. Test your guess by drawing the toothpick triangles. If you couldn't draw 7 triangles, revise your guess. Test your guess again. Keep trying.

   C. **Draw a diagram.**
      Draw a diagram of 3 triangles using 7 lines to represent toothpicks. Keep adding lines until you have 7 triangles. Count the number of lines.

2. The perimeter of one face of a cube is 28 cm. What is the surface area of the cube?

   A. **Write equations.**
      Calculate the length of one edge of the cube. Let n represent the length.
      $28 = 4n$
      The length of one edge of the cube is 7 cm.
      Calculate the area of one face. $A = 7 \cdot 7$
      Calculate the surface area of the cube. $S = 49 \cdot 6$

   B. **Guess and test.**
      Guess that the surface area of one face is 60 cm². Calculate that the area of one face is 10 cm². Calculate that the perimeter of one face is 40 cm. That guess didn't work, so make another guess.
      Guess that the surface area of one face is 42 cm². Calculate that the area of one face is 7 cm². So the perimeter of one face is 28 cm.

   C. **Work backward.**
      The perimeter of one face is 28 cm. So the length of one face is 14 cm.
      The area of one face would be $14 \cdot 14$.
      Then multiply that answer by 6 to calculate the surface area.

TRY IT

3. Kent is planting rows of seeds in the community garden. He plants 5 seeds in his first row, 11 seeds in his second row, and 17 seeds in his third row. If Kent uses the same pattern, how many seeds will he plant in his 7th row?

   A. **Write an equation.**
      $(1 \cdot 5) + (2 \cdot 11) + (3 \cdot 17) = ?$
      Calculate the number of seeds needed in each row and add them together.

   B. **Draw a diagram.**
      Draw 1 seed next to 5 seeds, then 2 seeds next to 11 seeds, and 3 seeds next to 17 seeds. Keep drawing and count all the seeds.

   C. **Make a table.**
      Write the seed-row numbers 1, 2, 3, 4, 5, 6, 7 as column names at the top of the table. In the first row of the table, write 5 in column 1, 11 in column 2, and 17 in column 3. Look for the pattern. Fill in the rest of the table using the same pattern.

4. Denzel can paint 12 tiles in an hour. How many tiles can Denzel paint in $4\frac{1}{2}$ hours?

   A. **Make a table.**
      Look for a pattern in your table.

Hours	1	2	3	4	5	6
Tiles	4.5	4.5	4.5	4.5	4.5	4.5

   B. **Write an equation.**
      Let n equal the number of tiles Denzel can paint in $4\frac{1}{2}$ hours.
      $n = 12 \cdot 4\frac{1}{2} = 12 \cdot \frac{9}{2} = \frac{108}{2} = 54$
      Denzel can paint 54 tiles in $4\frac{1}{2}$ hours.

   C. **Use simpler numbers.**
      Suppose that Denzel could paint only 10 tiles per hour. Calculate how many tiles he could paint in 4 hours. $10 \cdot 4 = 40$, so in 4 hours, he can paint 40 tiles.
      Now that you have figured out how to solve the problem, go back and solve it using fractions.

TRY IT

5. Maddie bought 3 more pounds of flour than Kath. Together Kath and Maddie bought 13 pounds of flour. How many pounds of flour did Kath buy?

A. **Guess and test.**
Guess that Kath bought 2 pounds of flour. This means that Maddie would have bought 5 pounds, because $2 + 3 = 5$. Add $2 + 5$. If the sum doesn't equal 13, revise your guess to be that Kath bought 3 pounds of flour. Figure out how many pounds of flour Maddie bought. Is this sum equal to 13? If not, revise your guess, and test your answer again.

B. **Draw a diagram.**
Draw 13 circles to represent the 13 pounds of flour. Divide the circles into two equal groups. Then multiply one group by 3.

C. **Write an equation.**
Let m represent the number pounds of flour Kath bought.
$(3 \cdot m) + 2 = 13$

6. Derek earned some money over the summer. He charged $7 to wash a car and $4 to walk a dog. He washed 12 cars and walked 6 dogs in August. How much money did Derek make in August?

A. **Work backward.**
Derek washed 12 cars so count backward from 12 to 7 to figure out how much money he made washing cars. He walked 6 dogs, so count back from 6 to 4 to see how much money he made walking dogs. Add the two amounts together.

B. **Write equations.**
Multiply the number of cars washed by the amount charged per car.
$12 \cdot 7 = 84$
Then multiply the number of dogs walked by the amount charged per dog. $6 \cdot 4 = 24$
Add the two products together to find the total amount earned.

C. **Draw a picture.**
Draw 12 cars and 6 dogs. Count the cars and dogs.

T R Y   I T

7. The animal park has 63 butterflies in a special environment for butterflies. There are 28 red butterflies, 19 white butterflies, and the rest are yellow. How many butterflies are yellow?

    A. **Write an equation.**
       $63 - 28 - 19 = ?$

    B. **Guess and test.**
       Guess that there are 20 yellow butterflies. Add 20 to the number of red and white butterflies. Is your answer 28? If not, revise your guess, and test your answer again.

    C. **Draw a diagram.**
       Draw 19 dots. Then figure out how many dots you need to get to 28 butterflies in all.

8. Charlotte was selling pies at a bake sale. She sold 13 pies before lunch and another 5 after lunch. At the end of the day, Charlotte had 8 pies left. How many pies did Charlotte start the day with?

    A. **Write an equation.**
       $8 + 5 - 13 = ?$

    B. **Draw a picture.**
       Draw 8 circles. Add 5 circles and then add 13 circles.

    C. **Guess and test.**
       Guess that Charlotte started with 20 pies. Subtract 8. Is your answer 13? If not, revise your guess, and test your answer again.

Mathematical Reasoning Methods (B)

Target 41 Game

Worked Examples

You can solve a complex story problem by using the guess-and-test strategy.
Read the following rules for earning points in the Target 41 dart game.

Scoring Rules for Target 41	
Sum of exactly 41	100 points
Darts land only on prime numbers	75 points
Sum of exactly 15	50 points
Sum of a tens number, such as 10, 20, 30, and so on	10 points
RULE: You may score in only one of these ways per turn.	

PROBLEM Trina, Daryl, and Janelle like to play the Target 41 dart game. When a player's darts land on numbered sections of the dartboard (shown below), the player uses those values to score points, as given on Scoring Rules for Target 41 above.

In one version of Target 41, each player gets 4 darts to throw. Trina, Daryl, and Janelle played a round of the 4-dart version. Trina and Daryl took their turns. Daryl had the higher score with 50 points, even though one of his darts didn't hit the board. Now it is Janelle's turn. She is eager to get a sum of 41 with her 4 darts so she can score 100 points. Find at least one way Janelle can reach a sum of 41.
Note: Multiple darts may land in the same numbered section.

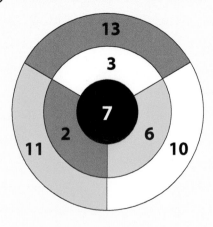

UNDERSTAND THE PROBLEM
You need to figure out what values Janelle's 4 darts can land on to get a sum of exactly 41.

DEVISE A PLAN
Use the guess-and-test strategy.

For each number on the target, label at least 4 index cards or slips of paper with that number. Arrange 4 cards at a time in different combinations to make guesses toward getting a sum of 41.

Use a table to organize your guesses and the results.

CARRY OUT THE PLAN
Make guesses like the ones shown in the following table:

Card 1	Card 2	Card 3	Card 4	Sum	Greater than or less than 41?
13	10	11	3	37	< 41; I need to make one of the addends greater.
13	10	11	6	40	< 41; I need to increase one of the addends by 1. I can change 10 to 11.
13	11	11	6	41	That's it!

LOOK BACK
Make sure you have answered the question that was asked. Have you found at least one way that Janelle can get a sum of 41?

ANSWER Janelle can get a sum of 41 with either of the following combinations:

$13 + 11 + 11 + 6 = 41$

$10 + 10 + 10 + 11 = 41$

L E A R N

Solve by using the target and the Scoring Rules for Target 41 in the Worked Examples.

1. Trina and Janelle are using as many darts as they want in a round against each other. Janelle has had a tough round, scoring only 10 points. Trina decides to try to make a sum of 15. Find at least 4 ways Trina can hit 15. **Note:** Multiple darts may land in the same section.

2. Daryl and Trina decide to play a round to score with only the prime numbers and no duplicates. They are using 4 darts each. Find at least 3 ways each player could hit the numbers on the target to score the 75 points for primes. **Note:** Multiple darts may **not** land in the same section.

3. While Daryl and Janelle were playing a round of Target 41, Daryl decided to find out how many ways he could get a total of 10 with no limit on the number of darts. Find at least 4 ways Daryl could get a total of 10. **Note:** Multiple darts may land in the same section.

4. Janelle is always challenging herself to hit 41 to score the most points, and she has created a game to make that goal even harder. In Janelle's game, players must do the following:

   • Use more than 4 darts
   • Get a sum of exactly 41
   • Not throw a dart that misses the board

   Find at least 3 ways a player could succeed at Janelle's game. **Note:** Multiple darts may land in the same section.

5. Use the information about the game in Problem 4. Find the greatest number of darts that can be used to succeed at Janelle's game.

Choose a problem-solving strategy. Explain how to solve the problem.

1. Erik's hockey team played 20 games last season. The team won 3 times as many games as it lost. It tied as many games as it lost.
   How many games did Erik's team win?

Choose the problem-solving strategy and explanation that correctly show how to solve the problem.

2. At the playground, Maribel stood on a raised platform and dropped a ball from a height of 14 feet. The ball bounced up half the distance. It then fell onto sand and stopped bouncing. How far did the ball travel?

   A. **Make a table.**
   Write first bounce. 14 ft
   Write second bounce. 7 ft
   Write third bounce. 3.5 ft
   Add the numbers.

   B. **Write an equation.**
   $(14 \div 2) + 14 \cdot 2 = d$
   Divide the distance from the top of the raised platform by 2. Add the distance from the top of the raised platform. Multiply that result by 2.

   C. **Draw a diagram.**
   Draw the path that the ball traveled and label the distances. The first distance is from the top of the raised platform to the bottom, which is 14 feet. The next distance is half of the first distance. The last distance is the ball's travel down, which is the same distance as the second distance. Add all the distances.

T R Y   I T

3. Raquel is 36 years old. Her son David is 8 years old. In how many years will Raquel be 3 times as old as David?

   A. **Make a table.**
   Write Raquel's age in 2-year increments on the top row.
   Raquel: 36, 38, 40, 42, 44
   Write her son's age in 2-year increments on the bottom row.
   David: 8, 10, 12, 14, 16
   Find when Raquel's age is 3 times David's age. Figure out how many years that will be from now.

   B. **Guess and test.**
   Guess that Raquel will be 46, and David will be 12 when she is 3 times as old as David. Divide 46 by 3. Is the answer 12? If not, revise your guess, and test your answer again.

   C. **Make a double bar graph.**
   Graph Raquel's age with one color and David's age with another color. Keep adding to the graph until you can see that one of the lines is 3 times as tall as the other.

4. The length of Erin's vegetable garden is 10.3 m, and the width is 6.1 m. She wants to double the width and halve the length of her garden. What will the area of Erin's new garden be?

   A. **Use simpler numbers.**
   Instead of using decimal numbers, round the numbers to the nearest whole number. Calculate $2 \cdot 6 = 12$ (estimating 2 times the width). Then calculate $10 \div 2 = 5$ $\left(\text{estimating } \frac{1}{2} \text{ the length}\right)$. Multiply these two products together: $12 \cdot 5 = 60$. The new area is about 60 m². Now that you have figured out how to solve the problem, go back and solve it, using decimal numbers.

   B. **Make a table.**
   Look for a pattern in your table.

Length	Width
11.3 m	6.1 m

   C. **Guess and test.**
   First guess that the area of the new garden will be 100 m². Figure out the length and the width. If the numbers are not correct, revise your guess, and test your answer again.

TRY IT

5. What number either subtracted from 111 or added to 75 would produce equal answers to both problems?

   A. **Write an equation.**
   Let *n* represent the number you don't know.
   $(111 + 75) \div 2 = n$

   B. **Draw a diagram.**
   Draw 111 dots. Also draw 75 dots. Keep crossing out dots until you have the same number of dots in both diagrams.

   C. **Guess and test.**
   Guess 20; $111 - 20 = 91$, and $75 + 20 = 95$. The answers are not equal.
   Guess 19; $111 - 19 = 92$, and $75 + 19 = 94$. The numbers are not equal but are getting closer. Revise your guess, and test your answer again.

6. James made 125 snowflakes and 115 colored balls. He wanted to divide the pieces evenly into 10 boxes. How many pieces should he put into each box?

   A. **Work backward.**
   Start with 125 snowflakes. Subtract the number of colored balls. Then multiply that answer by 10 because there are 10 boxes.

   B. **Guess and test.**
   Guess that the number of pieces in each box was 20. Multiply 20 by 10. Then add $125 + 115$. Are the two numbers the same? If not, revise your guess, and test your answer again.

   C. **Write an equation.**
   Add the numbers of the different pieces and then divide the total by 10.
   $(125 + 115) \div 10 = ?$

Choose the series of steps that will result in the correct answer.

7. Cassie has 6 times as many nickels as quarters. She has 3 more quarters than dimes. She has 8 dimes. How many nickels does Cassie have?

   A. Start with 6. Add 6 and 3. Then multiply that sum by 8.

   B. Start with 8. Add 8 and 3. Then multiply that sum by 6.

   C. Start with 8. Add 8 and 6. Then divide that sum by 3.

8. Jillian went shopping with her friend and at the end of the day she had $75.00 left over. She spent $14.95 on a book, $25.40 on some new shoes, and $35.75 on a new dress. How much money did Jillian have at the beginning?

   A. Start with $75.00. Add $14.95, $25.40, and $35.75.

   B. Start with $75.00. Add $14.95 and $25.40.

   C. Start with $75.00. Subtract $14.95, $25.40, and $35.75.

T R Y   I T

Mathematical Reasoning Methods (C)

Practice Solving Nonroutine Problems

Choose the problem-solving strategy and explanation that correctly show how to solve the problem.

1. Artie was saving pennies. On the first day, he saved 2 pennies. The next day, he saved twice as many, giving him a total of 6 pennies (2 + 4). He continued doubling the number of pennies he saved for 10 days. How many pennies did Artie have by the end of the 10th day?

   A. **Write an equation.**
      $10 \cdot (2 + 4) = b$
      Add the pennies he saved on the first and second days. Then multiply by the total number of days.

   B. **Make a table.**
      In the Day 1 column, write 2 pennies.
      In the Day 2 column, write 4 pennies.
      In the Day 3 column, write 8 pennies.
      Continue that pattern through Day 10. The solution is the sum of the numbers of pennies from each day.

   C. **Draw a diagram.**
      Draw 2 pennies and label them Day 1. Draw 6 pennies and label them Day 2. Draw 14 pennies and label them Day 3. Continue this pattern for the 10 days and then count all the pennies.

2. The temperature was 20°F at noon. The temperature increased 3°F per hour until 8:00 p.m. What was the temperature at 6:00 p.m.?

   A. **Guess and test.**
      Guess that the temperature will be 30°F. Find the difference between 20°F and 30°F and divide that by 3. If the answer is less than 6 (the number of hours between noon and 6:00 p.m.), revise your guess, and test your answer again.

   B. **Make a table.**
      Write noon, 1:00 p.m., 2:00 p.m., 3:00 p.m., 4:00 p.m., 5:00 p.m., and 6:00 p.m. on the top row. Write the temperature starting at 20°F under noon in the second row. Write the temperatures, increasing by 3°F, in the remaining boxes on the second row. The correct answer is the temperature at 6:00 p.m.

   C. **Work backward.**
      Start with 6:00 p.m. Subtract 6 hours from 6:00 p.m. to get to noon. Then multiply 20°F by 6 to find out the temperature at 6:00 p.m.

TRY IT

3. The surface area of a cube is 24 square inches. What is the perimeter of a face of the cube?

   A. **Guess and test.**
Guess that the perimeter of a face is 20 inches. This means that each side of a face is 5 inches. The area of each face would then be 25 square inches. Double that number to get the surface area. The product is greater than 24 square inches. Guess another number, and test it.

   B. **Write equations.**
Calculate the surface area of one face of the cube.
Let a represent the area of each face of the cube.
$24 = 6a$, so $4 = a$
Calculate the length of each side. Let s represent the length of each side of each face of the cube.
$s \cdot s = 4$, so $s = 2$
Calculate the perimeter of each face.
$P = 4 \cdot 2$

   C. **Work backward.**
Start with the surface area of 24. Divide by 4 to figure out the area of each face. Then multiply that answer by 4 to get the perimeter.

4. Julie wants to make a rectangular playground that has an area of 160 square feet. She wants to put a rope fence around it, but she wants to use as little rope as possible. What are the dimensions Julie should use for her playground?

   A. **Use objects to model the problem.**
Arrange 160 square tiles in different patterns until you get a rectangular shape. Count the number of tiles on the perimeter of this shape.

   B. **Write an equation.**
Write an equation that could be used to calculate the area of a rectangle. Use guess and check to find two numbers that when multiplied will give a product of 160.

   C. **Look for a pattern.**
Make a list of all possible combinations of length and width that would equal an area of 160 square feet. Then start calculating the perimeter of each rectangle. Look for a pattern to decrease the number of calculations you have to make.

Choose the series of steps that will result in the correct answer.

5. Timmy bought twice as many plums as apples. He bought 4 more plums than bananas. He bought 6 apples. How many bananas did Timmy buy?

   A. Start with 6. Multiply 6 by 2. Then subtract 4.

   B. Start with 6. Multiply 6 by 2. Then add 4.

   C. Start with 4. Add 4 and 6. Then multiply the sum by 2 and add 4.

6. A number is multiplied by 2. Then 8 is added to the product. The sum is then divided by 5. The answer is 8. What was the original number?

   A. Start with 8. Multiply 8 by 5. Then add 8 and multiply the sum by 2.

   B. Start with 8. Add 8 and 5. Then subtract 8 and multiply the sum by 2.

   C. Start with 8. Multiply 8 by 5. Then subtract 8 and divide the difference by 2.

Choose and Use Strategies (A)

Use Tables to Solve Problems

You can make a table as a strategy to find the solution to some story problems.

PROBLEM Nyree is 30 years old. Her daughter, Mia, is 6 years old. In how many years will Nyree be twice as old as Mia?

SOLUTION

UNDERSTAND THE PROBLEM
You know Nyree's age and Mia's age now. You need to compare their ages in future years.

DEVISE A PLAN
Use the make-a-table strategy. Put what you know in the table. Create a row for Nyree and a row for Mia. Put their ages now in the first column. To save time and space, have each new column stand for 2 years instead of 1 year.

CARRY OUT THE PLAN

Nyree's Age	30	32	34	36	38	40	42	44	46	48
Mia's Age	6	8	10	12	14	16	18	20	22	24

As you put ages in each column, check to see if Nyree's age is twice that of Mia. When you get to the column where that happens, stop and count the columns to the right of their current ages. Count each column as 2 years.

LOOK BACK
Look at the table and make sure you wrote the ages and counted the years correctly. Remember that each column of this table stands for 2 years.

ANSWER Nyree will be twice as old as her daughter in 18 years, when Nyree will be 48 years old and Mia will be 24 years old.

LEARN

Solve by making a table.

1. The temperature at 9:00 p.m. was 28°F. The temperature dropped 3°F each hour until 1:00 a.m. What was the temperature at 1:00 a.m.?

2. Cynthia bought 2 train tickets and a newspaper each day on the way to work. Each newspaper cost $2.50, and each train ticket cost $3.75. How much money did Cynthia spend in 10 days?

3. Ilene needs 2 cups of walnuts and 3 cups of almonds in her snack mix recipe. How many cups of nuts does she need to make 7 batches of snack mix?

4. Some soccer teams from a town are traveling to a tournament. Each team can have 3 coaches and 16 players. There are 12 coaches going to the tournament. How many players are going to the tournament?

LEARN

Choose and Use Strategies (A)

Practice Using Tables

Solve by making a table.

1. Peter is 35 years old. His son Nathan is 10 years old. How many years ago was Peter 6 times older than Nathan?

2. The temperature was 15° at noon. It increased 4°F per hour until 8:00 p.m. What was the temperature at 6:00 p.m.?

3. Tom bought a daisy and 2 roses for each of his 6 cousins. Daisies cost $1.25 each. Roses cost $2.99 each. How much money did Tom spend?

4. Charlie's bread recipe uses 1 cup of whole-wheat flour and 2 cups of white flour for each loaf. How many cups of flour does Charlie need to make 5 loaves of bread?

5. Toby is making a tile mosaic. He puts 3 blue tiles in the first row, 7 blue tiles in the second row, and 11 blue tiles in the third row. If Toby continues using the same pattern, how many blue tiles will he use in the 6th row?

6. Karly can make 1 square with 4 toothpicks. She can make 2 squares with 7 toothpicks. She can make 3 squares with 10 toothpicks. Karly continued making squares to the right of the toothpick squares shown.

   When Karly had made 9 squares in all, how many toothpicks had she used?

TRY IT

Write-an-Equation Strategy

Worked Examples

You can find the sum of consecutive even numbers by writing an equation.

PROBLEM Use an equation to find the sum of 2, 4, 6, 8, 10, and 12.

SOLUTION

UNDERSTAND THE PROBLEM

If you don't understand a word in the problem, look it up in a dictionary. The word *consecutive* means "following in order one after another."

If you were to restate this problem in your own words, you might say this: Use an equation to find the sum of the even whole numbers from 2 through 12.

DEVISE A PLAN

You can use an equation to solve the problem.

Background information on an equation to find the sum of consecutive numbers: Carl Friedrich Gauss was a mathematician and astronomer whose research, observations, and conclusions are important in the study of math. He was born in Germany in 1777. When he was a young boy, he came up with an equation to find the sum of consecutive numbers.

In his equation, the variable S stands for the sum. The variable n stands for how many numbers are in the group of consecutive numbers in the problem to be solved.

$$S = \frac{n(n + 1)}{2}$$

Look at Carl Friedrich Gauss's equation. Ask yourself: Would a similar equation work for adding consecutive **even** numbers quickly?

L E A R N

CARRY OUT THE PLAN

1 Compare a list of all consecutive whole numbers 1 through 12 with a list of consecutive even whole numbers 2 through 12:
- Consecutive even and odd numbers 1 through 12:
  1, 2, 3, 4, 5, 6, 7, 8, 9, 10, 11, 12
- Consecutive even numbers 2 through 12:
  2, 4, 6, 8, 10, 12

2 Look for a pattern in the ordered list of numbers.
- In the consecutive **even and odd** numbers, the third number is 3. In the consecutive **even** numbers, the third number is 6. The number 3 is half of 6.
- In the consecutive **even and odd** numbers, the fifth number is 5. In the consecutive **even** numbers, the fifth number is 10. The number 5 is half of 10.
- If you were to keep checking, you would see that every consecutive even number is twice its corresponding number in the ordered list of consecutive even and odd numbers. So the sums of the even numbers add up more quickly. In fact, they double.

3 Use what you have learned to write an equation to find the sum of consecutive even numbers.
- The following equation results in the sum of consecutive even and odd numbers when S stands for the sum and n stands for how many numbers you are finding the sum of:

$$S = \frac{n(n + 1)}{2}$$

- The sum of the consecutive even numbers will be 2 times greater than the sum of the consecutive even and odd numbers. So if you want the right side of the equation to represent twice its current value, you multiply that side by 2, which leaves 1 in the denominator of the fraction. The following equation now shows how to find the sum of consecutive **even** numbers:

$$S = n(n + 1)$$

4 You are trying to find the sum of the first 6 even numbers, so $n = 6$.

Substitute 6 for n.

$$S = n(n + 1)$$
$$S = 6(6 + 1)$$
$$S = 6(7)$$
$$S = 42$$

Using the equation, you find that the sum of the first 6 consecutive even numbers, 2, 4, 6, 8, 10, and 12, is 42.

LEARN

LOOK BACK

Another way to calculate the answer is to add the even numbers without using an equation. You can check your math by using an addition shortcut.

Draw arcs to number pairs that add to 14.

$$2 + 12 = 14 \qquad 4 + 10 = 14 \qquad 6 + 8 = 14$$

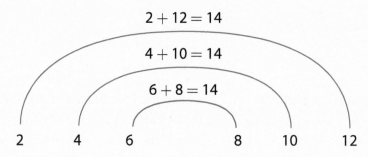

Then add how many sums of 14 there are altogether.

$$14 + 14 + 14 = 42$$

Using an addition shortcut, you find that the sum of the first 6 consecutive even numbers, 2, 4, 6, 8, 10, and 12, is 42.

ANSWER The sum of 2, 4, 6, 8, 10, and 12 is 42.

Use this equation for finding the sum of consecutive even numbers to solve the problem.

$$S = n(n + 1)$$

1. What is the sum of the consecutive even numbers 1 through 16?

2. What is the sum of the consecutive even numbers 1 through 30?

3. What is the sum of the consecutive even numbers 1 through 50?

4. What is the sum of the consecutive even numbers 1 through 62?

LEARN

Choose and Use Strategies (B)

Guess-and-Test Strategy

Worked Examples

You can guess numbers and test them to find answers to some story problems.

PROBLEM Mrs. Jensen has collected comic books for 10 years. Her daughter, Sara, just started a comic book collection. Mrs. Jensen has 24 times as many comic books as Sara has. Together, they have 225 comic books. How many comic books does each person have?

SOLUTION

UNDERSTAND THE PROBLEM
If you were to restate the problem in your own words, you might say this: The number of Sara's comic books multiplied by 24 equals the number of comic books Mrs. Jensen has. Together, they have 225 comic books. Find how many comic books each person has.

DEVISE A PLAN
This problem can be solved by the guess-and-test strategy. To make it easier to find the answer, you can combine the strategy with the write-an-equation strategy and the make-a-table strategy. You can use a table by putting your guesses into it.

CARRY OUT THE PLAN

1 Decide the variables that you'll use in the equations.
Represent Mrs. Jensen's comic books with the variable m.
Represent Sara's comic books with the variable d.

2 Translate this sentence into an equation: Mrs. Jensen has 24 times as many comic books as Sara has.
$d \cdot 24 = m$

3 Translate this sentence into an equation: Together, they have 225 comic books.
$m + d = 225$

L E A R N

4 You know that Sara has many fewer comic books than Mrs. Jensen has, so start by guessing a low number, such as 20, for Sara's number of comic books. Keep guessing. Multiply each guess by 24:

- First guess: $20 \cdot 24 = 480$. That's too high. You don't need to add the two numbers because you already know the second number is too high.
- Second guess: $10 \cdot 24 = 240$. That's still too high.
- Third guess: $5 \cdot 24 = 120$. Now you need to add 5 to 120 to show adding Sara's number of books to Mrs. Jensen's number of books. You get only 125 instead of 225. That's too low.
- Fourth guess: $9 \cdot 24 = 216$; $9 + 216 = 225$

You can keep track of your guesses in a table, such as the following one. When the product of the guessed number and 24 is more than 225, calculating the total is not needed.

First number	Second number	Total	Total too high, too low, or correct?
20	480	Not needed	Too high
10	240	Not needed	Too high
5	120	125	Too low
9	216	225	Correct

LOOK BACK
Check the math. Mrs. Jensen's 216 comic books and Sara's 9 comic books add up to 225. Mrs. Jensen's number of books is 24 times Sara's number.

ANSWER Mrs. Jensen has 216 comic books. Sara has 9 comic books.

Solve. Use the guess-and-test strategy combined with any other strategies you want to use. Use a table to show your work.

1. Joe started a coin collection by buying some coins. His father's coin collection contains 6 times as many coins as Joe has. The total number of coins they own is 49. How many coins does each person have?

2. Tom traveled 175 times as many miles to visit his grandmother as he traveled to visit his uncle. He traveled 2,816 miles in all. How many miles did Tom travel to visit each of his relatives?

Choose and Use Strategies (B)

Use Different Strategies

Solve. Use the write-an-equation strategy.

1. At the To-Go Pizza, each pizza costs $12 and each small salad costs $2. A delivery charge of $3 is added to every order. How much would it cost to have 6 pizzas and 3 small salads delivered?

2. At the art supply store, pastels cost $2.25, drawing pads cost $6.50, and pencils cost $1.17. Kelly bought 3 pastels, 2 drawing pads, and 12 pencils. How much money did Kelly spend?

3. Myra orders 3 beach balls and 2 sand castle kits from a catalog. The price of each beach ball is $4. The price of each sand castle kit is $10. Shipping costs for Myra's order are $6. What is the total cost of the order, including shipping?

4. Use the equation $S = n(n + 1)$ to find the sum of the consecutive even numbers through 40.

Solve. Use the guess-and-test strategy combined with any other strategies you want to use. Use a table to show your work.

5. Molly walked 6 more miles than Jeff on Sunday. They walked a total of 22 miles. How far did Jeff walk?

6. A DVD rental service keeps a record of the types of movies customers rent each day. Customers rented a total of 1,280 adventure movies and comedies on Saturday. They rented 19 times as many adventure movies as comedies. How many adventure movies did they rent on Saturday?

TRY IT

Choose and Use Strategies (C)

Practice Using Strategies

Memory Jogger

WORK BACKWARD

When you're given the "final" piece of information, you can often work backward to solve a story problem. You can use arrows and a set of steps to show how you worked backward from the last piece of information to find the answer.

Dacia has twice as many plants as Carol. Carol has 3 more plants than Sharon. Sharon has 2 fewer plants than Emily. Emily has 19 plants. How many plants does Dacia have?

Dacia has 40 plants.	←	Multiply by 2 to find how many plants Dacia has.	←	Add 3 to find how many plants Carol has.	←	Subtract 2 to find how many plants Sharon has.	←	Start with the number of plants Emily has.
		$20 \cdot 2 = 40$		$17 + 3 = 20$		$19 - 2 = 17$		19

Work backward to solve. Show your work using arrows and a set of steps.

1. David bought 3 more apples than oranges. He bought twice as many bananas as oranges, and he bought 5 more plums than bananas. David bought 17 plums. How many apples did David buy?

2. Ruby was selling melons at her fruit stand. She sold 13 melons in the morning. At lunchtime, 16 more melons were delivered to her. She then sold 19 more melons. At the end of the day, she had 11 melons left. How many melons did Ruby have at the start of the day?

TRY IT

Use any strategy you have learned to solve. Name the strategy. Show your work.

3. Percy bought 3 bottles of fruit juice and 2 packages of crackers. Bottles of fruit juice cost $1.49 each. Packages of crackers cost $0.89 each. How much did Percy spend?

4. Keiko has 3 more quarters than dimes. She has 2 times as many nickels as dimes. She has $2.00 in quarters. How much money does Keiko have?

5. Rachael's soccer game starts at 11 a.m. Her coach wants her to arrive 20 minutes before the game starts. It takes her 15 minutes to get to the game. She needs $1\frac{1}{2}$ hours to eat breakfast, get ready, and do her chores. What is the latest time that Rachael can get up in the morning so that she gets to her game on time?

Choose the answer.

6. Alex can read 22 pages of his book in an hour. How many pages can Alex read in 4.35 hours?

   A. **Substitute simpler numbers.**

      Suppose that Alex can read 20 pages in 1 hour. Calculate how many pages he could read in 4 hours: $20 \cdot 4 = 80$. So in 4 hours he can read 80 pages. Now that you have figured out how to solve the problem, go back and solve it using fractions.

   B. **Work backward.**

      Start with 4.25 hours. Subtract 22 pages to see how many sets of 22 are in 4.25 hours.

   C. **Make a table.**

      Look for a pattern in your table.

Hour	1	2	3	4	5	6
Pages	22	22	22	22	22	22

TRY IT

Solve Simple to Complex Problems (A)

Solve One-Step Story Problems

Worked Examples

You can use the problem-solving plan to solve simple one-step story problems with mixed numbers.

PROBLEM 1 Billy ran $1\frac{3}{4}$ miles on Monday and $2\frac{1}{2}$ miles on Tuesday. How many miles did he run in all?

SOLUTION

UNDERSTAND THE PROBLEM
List the important numbers in the problem and figure out what operations you will use. The important numbers are $1\frac{3}{4}$ and $2\frac{1}{2}$. You will use addition.

DEVISE A PLAN
Write an equation. Compare the denominators in the mixed numbers to see if one or both of them need to be changed.

CARRY OUT THE PLAN

1 Write the equation. The variable n represents the total miles run. $\longrightarrow$ $1\frac{3}{4} + 2\frac{1}{2} = n$

2 Find the least common denominator (LCD) of the fractions $\frac{3}{4}$ and $\frac{1}{2}$. The LCD of the two fractions is 4. $\longrightarrow$ $\frac{1}{2} = \frac{2}{4}$

3 Change $2\frac{1}{2}$ to $2\frac{2}{4}$ in the equation and add. $\longrightarrow$ $1\frac{3}{4} + 2\frac{2}{4} = 3\frac{5}{4}$

4 Simplify. $\longrightarrow$ $3\frac{5}{4} = 4\frac{1}{4}$

LOOK BACK
Check that the answer makes sense. You can estimate that Billy ran about 2 miles each day, so the answer should be about 4 miles.

ANSWER Billy ran a total of $4\frac{1}{4}$ miles Monday and Tuesday.

Solve. Express in simplest mixed-number form.

1. The Kelly family went shopping. They drove for $3\frac{1}{2}$ miles to one store and $2\frac{3}{4}$ miles to another store. How many miles did they drive in all?

2. Colin hiked for $3\frac{2}{3}$ miles one weekend. The next weekend, he hiked for $2\frac{2}{3}$ miles. How many miles did he hike?

L E A R N

You can use the problem-solving plan to solve more complex one-step story problems with fractions and mixed numbers in the same way you solved the simpler problems.

PROBLEM 2 Steve likes to ride his bike on a trail near his home. He lives $\frac{7}{10}$ of a mile from a bike trail. On Saturday, he rode $2\frac{1}{2}$ miles. On Sunday, he rode $3\frac{2}{3}$ miles. On Monday, he rode $3\frac{4}{6}$ miles. How far did Steve ride in all?

SOLUTION

UNDERSTAND THE PROBLEM

This problem is more complex than the problem in the previous Worked Example, but you can use the same method to solve it.

The important numbers in this problem are $2\frac{1}{2}$, $3\frac{2}{3}$, and $3\frac{4}{6}$. You will use addition.

DEVISE A PLAN

As in the previous Worked Example, you can solve this problem by writing an equation.

CARRY OUT THE PLAN

1 Write the equation. The variable n represents the total miles ridden. $\longrightarrow$ $2\frac{1}{2} + 3\frac{2}{3} + 3\frac{4}{6} = n$

2 Find the least common denominator (LCD) of the fractions $\frac{1}{2}$, $\frac{2}{3}$, and $\frac{4}{6}$. The LCD is 6. $\longrightarrow$ $\frac{3}{6}, \frac{4}{6}, \frac{4}{6}$

3 Put the equivalent mixed numbers in the equation and add. $\longrightarrow$ $2\frac{3}{6} + 3\frac{4}{6} + 3\frac{4}{6} = 8\frac{11}{6}$

4 Simplify. $\longrightarrow$ $8\frac{11}{6} = 9\frac{5}{6}$

LOOK BACK

Check that the answer makes sense. You can estimate that Steve rode about $2\frac{1}{2}$, $3\frac{1}{2}$, and $3\frac{1}{2}$ miles for a total of about $9\frac{1}{2}$ miles. The exact answer is close to that estimate.

ANSWER Steve rode $9\frac{5}{6}$ miles during the 3 days.

Solve. Express in simplest mixed-number form.

3. Tara's soccer team went out for pizza. They ate $8\frac{2}{3}$ pizzas. Last week, they ate $6\frac{3}{9}$ pizzas. How many more pizzas did they eat this week?

4. Peter's team went out to eat twice after games. Both times, the team ate 24-inch sandwiches. The first week, they ate $3\frac{1}{2}$ sandwiches. The second week, they ate $4\frac{7}{10}$ sandwiches. How many more sandwiches did they eat the second week than the first week?

L E A R N

Solve Simple to Complex Problems (A)

Solve Multistep Story Problems

Worked Examples

You can use the problem-solving plan to solve simple multistep story problems with fractions and mixed numbers.

PROBLEM 1 Every week, Tommy buys $1\frac{1}{3}$ pounds of turkey and $2\frac{2}{3}$ pounds of cheese. How much turkey and cheese would he buy in 6 weeks?

SOLUTION

UNDERSTAND THE PROBLEM
Find the important numbers in the problem and figure out what operations you will use. The important numbers are $1\frac{1}{3}$, $2\frac{2}{3}$, and 6. You will use addition and multiplication. You might restate the problem as follows: If Tommy buys $1\frac{1}{3}$ pounds plus $2\frac{2}{3}$ pounds of those food items each week for 6 weeks, how many total pounds would he buy?

DEVISE A PLAN
Write an equation. Change the mixed numbers to improper fractions. Add them. Multiply the sum by 6.

CARRY OUT THE PLAN

1 Write an equation. The variable n represents the total amount of food in 1 week. $\longrightarrow$ $1\frac{1}{3} + 2\frac{2}{3} = n$

2 Add. $\longrightarrow$ $1\frac{1}{3} + 2\frac{2}{3} = 4$

3 Write another equation. The variable n represents $\longrightarrow$ $n = 4 \cdot 6$ the total amount of food in 6 weeks.

4 Multiply. $\longrightarrow$ $n = 24$

LOOK BACK
Double-check the math and look at the story problem to see if the answer is reasonable. A quick estimate would be $(1 + 3)6$, or 24, which is also the exact answer.

ANSWER Tommy would buy 24 pounds of turkey and cheese in 6 weeks.

LEARN

You can use the problem-solving plan to solve more complex multistep story problems with fractions and mixed numbers in the same way you solved the simpler problems.

PROBLEM 2 Tommy bought $2\frac{8}{10}$ pounds of cheddar cheese. He bought $1\frac{6}{8}$ fewer pounds of American cheese than cheddar cheese. He bought the same amount of the same cheeses for 5 weeks. How much American cheese did he buy in 5 weeks?

SOLUTION

UNDERSTAND THE PROBLEM
Find the important numbers in the problem and figure out what operations you will use. The important numbers are $2\frac{8}{10}$, $1\frac{6}{8}$, and 5. You will use subtraction and multiplication.

DEVISE A PLAN
You need to subtract to find out how much American cheese Tommy buys each week and then multiply that amount over 5 weeks.

You can refer to the simpler problems in the previous Worked Example. This problem is similar but has more steps.

CARRY OUT THE PLAN

1 Find out how many pounds of American cheese Tommy bought each week.

- Write equation. The variable *n* represents the total amount of American cheese in 1 week. $\longrightarrow$ $2\frac{8}{10} - 1\frac{6}{8} = n$

- Find the least common denominator for the mixed numbers. $\longrightarrow$ $2\frac{32}{40} - 1\frac{30}{40} = n$

- Subtract the whole numbers and the fractions. $\longrightarrow$ $2\frac{32}{40} - 1\frac{30}{40} = 1\frac{2}{40}$

- Simplify. $\longrightarrow$ $1\frac{2}{40} = 1\frac{1}{20}$

Tommy bought $1\frac{1}{20}$ pounds of American cheese every week.

2 Find out how many pounds of American cheese Tommy bought over 5 weeks.

- Write equation. The variable *n* represents the total amount of American cheese in 5 weeks. $\longrightarrow$ $1\frac{1}{20} \cdot 5 = n$

- Change the mixed number to an improper fraction. $\longrightarrow$ $\frac{21}{20} \cdot \frac{5}{1} = n$

- Multiply. $\longrightarrow$ $\frac{21}{4} \cdot \frac{1}{1} = \frac{21}{4}$

- Simplify. $\longrightarrow$ $\frac{21}{4} = 5\frac{1}{4}$

L E A R N

LOOK BACK

Check to see if the answer seems reasonable. When you look back at the problem, you can estimate that 3 pounds minus 2 pounds is 1 pound, and 1 • 5 equals 5. The exact answer of $5\frac{1}{4}$ is close to 5.

ANSWER Tommy bought $5\frac{1}{4}$ pounds of American cheese in 5 weeks.

Solve. Express in simplest mixed-number form.

1. Katie buys $2\frac{2}{4}$ pounds of grapes and $1\frac{1}{3}$ pounds of pears each week. How much fruit would she buy in 4 weeks?

2. In January, Betsy volunteered for $5\frac{3}{4}$ hours at the library. In February, she volunteered $1\frac{2}{3}$ fewer hours. In March, she volunteered $4\frac{1}{2}$ more hours than in February. How many hours did she volunteer in March?

3. Adam ran the same amount each day for 4 days. He ran a total of $7\frac{1}{5}$ miles. The first day, he also walked $2\frac{3}{8}$ miles. How far did he run and walk on the first day?

LEARN

Solve Simple to Complex Problems (B)

Fractions as Decimals in Story Problems

Worked Examples

You can use the problem-solving plan to solve story problems that include changing fractions and mixed numbers to decimal numbers.

PROBLEM Sophia bought $3\frac{1}{5}$ meters of ribbon. Ribbon costs $1.05 a meter. How much did Sophia spend?

SOLUTION

UNDERSTAND THE PROBLEM

You might restate the problem by saying that Sophia bought $3\frac{1}{5}$ meters of ribbon for $1.05 a meter, and you need to know how much she spent on ribbon. The operation you will use is multiplication.

DEVISE A PLAN

You will need to figure out how to change the mixed number to a decimal number. You will then need to write equations so you can multiply the decimal number you computed by the one already in the problem ($1.05) and solve the problem.

CARRY OUT THE PLAN

1 Change $3\frac{1}{5}$ to a decimal number.

$3\frac{1}{5} = 3.2$

2 Use the variable n to represent the money Sophia spent. Write an equation.

$n = 3.2 \cdot \$1.05$

$n = \$3.36$

LOOK BACK

Make sure that the answer is reasonable. For an estimate, think: Sophia bought about 3 meters of ribbon for about $1.00 a meter for a total cost of $3.00, so the answer of $3.36 is reasonable.

ANSWER Sophia spent $3.36 on ribbon.

LEARN

Solve.

1. Jenny bought $2\frac{1}{2}$ yards of blue ribbon and $4\frac{3}{4}$ yards of yellow ribbon. The ribbon costs $1.50 a yard. How much did Jenny spend on ribbon?

2. Sam needed flannel to make a blanket for his parents. He bought $1\frac{1}{4}$ yards of purple flannel and $1\frac{3}{6}$ yards of black flannel. The flannel costs $2.40 a yard. How much did Sam spend on flannel?

3. Kevin bought decorative ribbon for a parade. He got to the store at 7:00 p.m., and it took him 15 minutes to check out. He bought $5\frac{1}{5}$ meters of purple polka-dot ribbon and $6\frac{1}{4}$ meters of red-and-white striped ribbon. The decorative ribbon costs $2.60 a meter. How much did Kevin spend on ribbon?

4. Amy bought fabric to make curtains. She bought $2\frac{1}{4}$ feet for one window and $3\frac{3}{12}$ feet for another window. She will be using blinds on her other three windows, which measure $3\frac{1}{5}$ feet, $3\frac{1}{2}$ feet, and $2\frac{3}{8}$ feet. The fabric for her curtains costs $8.15 a foot. How much did Amy spend on fabric?

Solve Simple to Complex Problems (B)

Convert Measurements in Story Problems

Worked Examples

You can use the problem-solving plan to solve multistep story problems that include converting one unit of measure to another.

PROBLEM Martin filled canteens with $3\frac{8}{10}$ gallons of water for his hiking group to drink during a hike. One gallon of water weighs about 8.35 pounds. How many pounds of water did Martin's hiking group take on the hike?

SOLUTION

UNDERSTAND THE PROBLEM

Ask yourself what you need to find, explain, or show. You need to find the number of pounds of water Martin's hiking group took, and you need to convert gallons to pounds to get the answer.

Restate the problem. Martin's hiking group took $3\frac{8}{10}$ gallons of water at about 8.35 pounds per gallon, and you will find out how many pounds of water the group took on the hike.

Figure out what operation to use. You will use multiplication.

DEVISE A PLAN

To solve the problem, you will need to change $3\frac{8}{10}$ to a decimal number because the weight of the water is given as a decimal number. Then you will need to multiply the number of gallons of water by the weight of 1 gallon of water.

CARRY OUT THE PLAN

1 Change $3\frac{8}{10}$ to a decimal number. $3\frac{8}{10} = 3.8$

2 Recall that 1 gallon of water weighs about 8.35 pounds. Let n represent the amount of water Martin's hiking group took on the hike.

$n = 3.8 \cdot 8.35$

$n = 31.73$

LOOK BACK

Make sure that the answer is reasonable. For an estimate, think: $3\frac{8}{10}$ gallons is close to 4 gallons, and 8.35 pounds is close to 8 pounds. $4 \cdot 8 = 32$, so the answer of 31.73 is reasonable.

ANSWER Martin's hiking group took about 31.73 pounds of water on the hike.

L E A R N

Solve.

1. Bella and her family are at a picnic. She brought a jug filled with $2\frac{9}{10}$ gallons of water. Her uncle brought another jug that held $4\frac{7}{10}$ gallons of water. One gallon of water weighs about 8.35 pounds. Bella's aunt brought $\frac{1}{4}$ gallon of water. How many pounds of water did Bella and her uncle bring to the picnic?

2. Kelsey has two music playlists on her MP3 player that she wants to combine. The first playlist is 12 minutes and 51 seconds long. The second is 15 minutes and 38 seconds. The songs on the playlists average 3 minutes and 15 seconds. How many seconds of music will Kelsey have when she combines the two playlists? (**Hint:** 1 minute = 60 seconds)

3. Mary's family is making a macaroni-and-cheese dish and homemade ice cream for a team picnic. Each batch of macaroni and cheese calls for $2\frac{1}{2}$ cups of milk. Each batch of ice cream calls for $3\frac{1}{4}$ cups of milk. Her family needs to make 4 batches of each. How many quarts of milk does Mary's family need? (**Hint:** 1 quart = 4 cups)

4. Paul's family is going to the soccer team party. They are taking $1\frac{3}{4}$ pounds of fruit salad for each family and $\frac{1}{4}$ pounds of bagel chips for each family. There are 12 families. Each family has at least 4 people and at least 1 boy. How many ounces of fruit salad and bagel chips will Paul's family take to the party? (**Hint:** 16 ounces = 1 pound)

LEARN

Solve Problems Logically (A)

Solve Equal-Measures Problems

Worked Examples

You can use the problem-solving plan to solve story problems about items or measurements that are equally grouped, also known as equal-measures problems.

PROBLEM Susan bought 50 inches of red ribbon and 20 inches of white ribbon. She wants to use equal amounts of both types of ribbon in 5 projects. What is the difference in length between one piece of red ribbon and one piece of white ribbon?

SOLUTION

UNDERSTAND THE PROBLEM
You know the length of the red ribbon and the white ribbon and that they are each divided into equal-sized pieces. You know that both colors of ribbon are shared among 5 projects. You need to find out the difference in length between the two colors of ribbon.

If you were to restate the problem in your own words, you might say this: Share 50 inches of red ribbon and 20 inches of white ribbon among 5 projects by separating each color of ribbon into equal-sized pieces. Find out the difference in length between a piece of red ribbon and a piece of white ribbon.

DEVISE A PLAN
Use equations to solve the problem.

Divide the total amount of red ribbon by 5. Divide the total amount of white ribbon by 5. Subtract the lesser quotient from the greater one.

CARRY OUT THE PLAN

1. Find the length of each piece of red ribbon. $50 \div 5 = 10$

2. Find the length of each piece of white ribbon. $20 \div 5 = 4$

3. Subtract the lesser amount from the greater amount. $10 - 4 = 6$

LOOK BACK
Check that the answer is reasonable and that clear and logical steps were used to find the solution. Susan bought a little more than twice as much red ribbon as white ribbon, so it makes sense that one piece of red ribbon is a little more than twice as long as one piece of white ribbon.

ANSWER The difference in length between one piece of red ribbon and one piece of white ribbon is 6 inches.

L E A R N

Write a sequence of steps to solve the problem.

1. Mr. Keefer is a truck driver. He drives 450 miles a day, 250 days each year. His truck can drive 15 miles on each gallon of gas. How many gallons of gas does Mr. Keefer's truck use each year?

2. Tommy is having snacks with his friends. Among the friends, 7 want to eat raisins and 5 want to eat banana chips. Raisins and banana chips are sold in 3-ounce bags. How many more ounces of raisins than banana chips will Tommy's friends eat?

3. Cindy bought 120 grams of chicken and 212 grams of turkey. She wants to divide each type of meat into 4 equal servings. What is the difference in weight between one serving of chicken and one serving of turkey?

4. Kim bought 2 feet of pine wood at $4.82 per foot. She also bought 4 feet of maple wood at $3.17 per foot. What is the total cost of Kim's purchases?

Solve Problems Logically (B)

Solve Rate Story Problems

Worked Examples

You can use the problem-solving plan and clear and logical steps to solve story problems about rates.

PROBLEM Tommy needs to buy 12 pounds of oranges for a snack for his outdoor explorers club. He can buy oranges in two different ways:

1 Buy oranges by the bag. Each bag has 3 pounds of oranges and costs $4.26.

2 Buy oranges for $1.56 per pound.

What is the less expensive rate, and how much money will he save if he buys 12 pounds of oranges in the less expensive way?

SOLUTION

UNDERSTAND THE PROBLEM
You know that Tommy can buy oranges by the bag at a rate of $4.26 for 3 pounds. He can also buy oranges for $1.56 per pound.

You need to find out which rate for oranges is less expensive and how much difference there is between the more expensive rate and the less expensive rate. You need all the information that is given in the problem.

If you were to restate the problem, you might say this: Tommy needs to know the price difference between 12 pounds of oranges priced at 3 pounds for $4.26 and 12 pounds of oranges priced at $1.56 per pound.

DEVISE A PLAN
Use equations to solve the problem. To compare prices that are given as rates, make both rates the same, such as per pound in this problem.

1 Divide to find the price per pound of oranges in the 3-pound bags.

2 Multiply to find how much 12 pounds of oranges would cost at that rate.

3 Multiply to find the price of 12 pounds of oranges at the rate of $1.56 per pound.

4 Note that the greater product is the price of the more expensive oranges.

5 Subtract the lesser product from the greater product to find how much money Tommy will save.

LEARN

In this problem, it doesn't matter in which order you calculate the two rates. But you need to find the different costs per pound before you can find the costs for 12 pounds of oranges at each rate. You must find the costs for 12 pounds of oranges at the two different rates before you find how much Tommy will save.

CARRY OUT THE PLAN

1 Find the price per pound of oranges in the 3-pound bags.
Divide. $4.26 ÷ 3 = $1.42
Oranges in the bag cost $1.42 per pound.

2 Find how much 12 pounds of oranges cost at $1.42 per pound.
Multiply. $1.42 • 12 = $17.04
Now you know that 12 pounds of oranges bought in 3-pound bags cost $17.04.

3 Find the price of 12 pounds of oranges sold at $1.56 per pound.
Multiply. $1.56 • 12 = $18.72
Now you know that 12 pounds of oranges bought by the pound cost $18.72.

4 Note that it costs $17.04 to buy 12 pounds of oranges that cost $1.42 per pound. It costs $18.72 to buy 12 pounds of oranges that cost $1.56 per pound.

5 Calculate the difference in price between the oranges sold at the different rates.
Subtract. $18.72 − $17.04 = $1.68

LOOK BACK

Check that you used clear and logical steps to find the solution, that you answered the question, and that the answer is reasonable.

The answer is reasonable because $1.42 per pound and $1.56 per pound are close to each other, so there is only a small difference between the cost of the more expensive and the less expensive oranges.

You can also use estimation to check the reasonableness:

- $1.42 rounded to the nearest 10 cents is $1.40.
- $1.56 rounded to the nearest 10 cents is $1.60.
- The estimated difference in the rates is $0.20.
- 12 pounds rounded to the nearest 10 is 10 pounds.
- Multiply the estimated difference in the rates by the rounded number of pounds. $0.20 • 10 = $2.00

The estimated difference between the more expensive and less expensive oranges is about $2.00. The exact answer, $1.68, rounded to the nearest dollar is $2.00, which is the same as the estimate.

ANSWER The less expensive oranges are the ones sold in 3-pound bags for $4.26 per bag. Tommy will save $1.68 if he buys 12 pounds of oranges in the 3-pound bags.

Write a sequence of steps to solve the problem. Briefly explain each step.

1. Lucy is a pilot. She flies for 1,400 hours each year and travels 1,260,000 km. Paul is also a pilot. He flies for 1,200 hours each year and travels 1,110,000 km. Who flies at a faster rate, and how much faster is that rate compared with the slower rate?

2. Bob likes to ride his bike around the lake. He bikes 18 miles at an average speed of 12 miles per hour. He started biking at 10:15 a.m. today. What time will it be when Bob finishes his bike ride?

3. A local farmers market is selling blueberries at 2 pounds for $6.00. Steve wants to buy 3 pounds. How much will 3 pounds of blueberries cost?

4. Amy took a car trip to visit a national park. She wanted her car to be fuel efficient and use gas at a rate of at least 26 miles per gallon. When she returned home, Amy found that she had driven 2,356 miles and used 77.5 gallons of gas. Did Amy meet her goal? Explain.

LEARN

Estimation and Reasonable Answers

Reasonable Answers

You can use the problem-solving plan to help you decide if an answer is reasonable.

PROBLEM Samantha read the following problem:

Mr. Miller has driving directions from his home to a hardware store. The store opens at 8:00 a.m. The directions tell him to drive on Elm Street for $3\frac{7}{10}$ miles, turn right, and then drive on North Street for $3\frac{1}{5}$ miles to reach the store. What is the total distance from Mr. Miller's home to the hardware store?

Samantha calculated the answer this way: $3\frac{7}{10} + 3\frac{1}{5} = 3\frac{9}{10}$

Is her answer reasonable?

SOLUTION

UNDERSTAND THE PROBLEM

To restate the problem, you could say that you need to find out if $3\frac{9}{10}$ is a reasonable answer to the story problem. The story problem asks for the total distance of Mr. Miller's drive. The distances given in the story problem are $3\frac{7}{10}$ and $3\frac{1}{5}$.

The problem gives information that you don't need. You don't need to know when the store opens.

DEVISE A PLAN

For your plan, start by checking Samantha's plan. See if you agree with addition as the operation. You can then use a number line to estimate the answer to see if Samantha's answer is reasonable.

CARRY OUT THE PLAN

1. Note that Samantha used addition to solve the problem. Addition seems reasonable because the directions say Mr. Miller will drive some miles and then drive more miles. Samantha added $3\frac{7}{10}$ miles and $3\frac{1}{5}$ miles to get $3\frac{9}{10}$ miles.

LEARN

2 Look at a number line from 2 to 8 in intervals of $\frac{1}{4}$, such as 2, $2\frac{1}{4}$, $2\frac{1}{2}$, $2\frac{3}{4}$, 3, and so on.

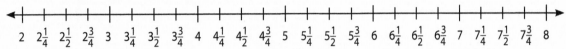

2   $2\frac{1}{4}$ $2\frac{1}{2}$ $2\frac{3}{4}$ 3 $3\frac{1}{4}$ $3\frac{1}{2}$ $3\frac{3}{4}$ 4 $4\frac{1}{4}$ $4\frac{1}{2}$ $4\frac{3}{4}$ 5 $5\frac{1}{4}$ $5\frac{1}{2}$ $5\frac{3}{4}$ 6 $6\frac{1}{4}$ $6\frac{1}{2}$ $6\frac{3}{4}$ 7 $7\frac{1}{4}$ $7\frac{1}{2}$ $7\frac{3}{4}$ 8

- $3\frac{3}{4}$ is the closest benchmark number greater than $3\frac{7}{10}$. Locate $3\frac{3}{4}$ on the number line.
- $3\frac{1}{4}$ is the closest benchmark number greater than $3\frac{1}{5}$. Count $3\frac{1}{4}$ units beyond $3\frac{3}{4}$. You end up at 7 on the number line.
- The estimated sum of $3\frac{7}{10}$ and $3\frac{1}{5}$ is 7, so the estimated distance from Mr. Miller's home to the hardware store is 7 miles.

3 Remember that Samantha's answer was $3\frac{9}{10}$ miles. Your estimate was 7 miles. Something's not right. Her answer is not reasonable.

4 Check the math in Samantha's solution.

Add the two distances.

$3\frac{7}{10} + 3\frac{1}{5} = 3\frac{7}{10} + 3\frac{2}{10} = 6\frac{9}{10}$

Samantha added the fractions together but forgot to add **both** of the whole-number parts, 3 and 3. She only added one whole number.

LOOK BACK

Review that Samantha's answer, $3\frac{9}{10}$, is not reasonable. Your estimate was 7, and those two numbers are not reasonably close. You used the number line to estimate that 7 was the answer. Your exact answer is $6\frac{9}{10}$, so your estimate and the exact answer are close. In fact, if you round the exact answer, $6\frac{9}{10}$, to the nearest whole number, it rounds to 7, which is the same as the estimate. So your answer makes sense and is reasonable.

ANSWER Samantha's answer isn't reasonable. The exact answer is $6\frac{9}{10}$ miles.

LEARN

Use estimation to find out if the answer is reasonable. Explain.

1. Hector read this problem:

   Patsy is making trail mix. She needs $4\frac{1}{2}$ cups of granola, $1\frac{2}{7}$ cups of raisins, and $\frac{5}{6}$ cup of chocolate chips for each batch. How many more cups of granola than raisins does she need?

   Hector calculated the answer this way: $4\frac{1}{2} - 1\frac{2}{7} = 3\frac{3}{14}$

   Is his answer reasonable?

2. Anna solved this problem and said the answer was $7\frac{7}{8}$ feet:

   Molly had a piece of lace $4\frac{3}{4}$ feet long. She used $1\frac{1}{8}$ feet for a sewing project and gave her sister $2\frac{1}{4}$ feet to use on a pillow. How much lace did Molly have left?

   Is Anna's answer reasonable?

3. Jack solved this problem and said the answer was $1\frac{1}{10}$ feet:

   Trent cut two pieces of wood. One piece of wood was $3\frac{4}{5}$ feet long. He also cut a piece of wood that was $4\frac{7}{10}$ feet long. What was the total length of both pieces of wood?

   Is Jack's answer reasonable?

L E A R N

Mean, Median, and Mode

Find and Apply the Mean to Data

Worked Examples

If you know the mean of a set of data, you can find a missing data point.

PROBLEM The table shows the daily attendance at a 4-day series of free concerts in a park.

The mean attendance for the four concerts was 61. How many people attended the concert on Sunday?

Attendance at Free Concerts	
Day	**Number of people**
Thursday	31
Friday	45
Saturday	89
Sunday	?

SOLUTION

1 Write an equation to solve the problem. In the equation, M stands for the mean number of people who attended the concerts during the 4 days, while x stands for the number of people who attended the concert on Sunday.

$$M = \frac{31 + 45 + 89 + x}{4}$$

2 Substitute 61 for M.

$$61 = \frac{31 + 45 + 89 + x}{4}$$

3 Use algebra to find the value of x. Multiply both sides of the equation by 4 to change the fraction on the right side of the equals sign to an expression without a denominator. Multiplication by 4 is the inverse operation of division by 4.

$$61 \cdot 4 = \frac{31 + 45 + 89 + x}{4} \cdot 4$$
$$61 \cdot 4 = 31 + 45 + 89 + x$$

4 Complete the multiplication on the left side of the equation.

$$244 = 31 + 45 + 89 + x$$

5 Add the numbers on the right side of the equation. The variable x remains.

$$244 = 165 + x$$

6 Subtract 165 from both sides of the equation and simplify.

$$244 - 165 = 165 - 165 + x$$
$$79 = x$$

ANSWER The attendance on Sunday was 79.

LOOK BACK Substitute 79 for x in the equation in Step 2 to check your answer. When you add 31, 45, 89, and 79 and divide the sum by 4, you get 61. The given mean was 61, so 79 is the correct answer for the missing data point.

L E A R N

Use the mean to find the missing data point in a set of data.

1. Umbrella rentals at a beach stand each day during a 5-day period are given in the table.

Umbrellas Rented	
Day	**Number rented**
Monday	25
Tuesday	36
Wednesday	42
Thursday	56
Friday	?

The mean number of umbrellas rented during the 5-day period was 49. How many umbrellas were rented on Friday?

2. Snow-cone sales at a snack stand each day during a 7-day period are given in the table.

Snow Cones Sold	
Day	**Number sold**
Sunday	?
Monday	35
Tuesday	62
Wednesday	27
Thursday	81
Friday	92
Saturday	106

The mean number of snow cones sold during the 7-day period was 70. How many snow cones were sold on Sunday?

3. Lawn chairs set up for an outdoor show each day for a 6-day period are given in the table.

Lawn Chairs for the Outdoor Show	
Day	**Lawn chairs**
June 4	82
June 5	?
June 6	79
June 7	87
June 8	90
June 9	111

The mean number of lawn chairs set up during the 6-day period was 87. How many lawn chairs were set up on June 5?

Mean, Median, and Mode

Create a Data Set

Worked Examples

You can create a data set that follows given rules.

PROBLEM Create a data set that has five data points, a range of 9, and one mode.

SOLUTION There are many data sets that could be created with this information. One example that would follow the rules is shown here. When you create a data set, draw a set of blank lines to begin. Number your steps. Write the values in order from the least value on the left to the greatest value on the right.

1 **Start with five data points.**
Drawing five blank lines will help you keep track of the values in the data set. Show one blank line for each of the values. Put commas between the blank lines.

___ , ___ , ___ , ___ , ___

2 **Use a range of 9.**
The range of a set of data shows the difference between the greatest value and the least value. For this data set, you could use 9 as the least value and 18 as the greatest value. Because $18 - 9 = 9$, the range is 9.

9 , ___ , ___ , ___ , 18

3 **Make the set have one mode.**
The value or values that occur most often in a data set are the mode. A data set can have more than one mode. This data set has only one mode. You could choose 11 as the mode and show it twice.

9 , ___ , 11 , 11 , 18

4 **Complete the data set.**
One more value is needed to complete the data set. At this point in solving the problem, the data set has values that meet all the requirements of the problem. That means you must choose the last value carefully. You can't choose 9 or 18 for the last value because then there would be two modes.

You could choose 10 or 11 to complete the data set. There would still be five data points, a range of 9, and one mode. (You could also remove the blank between 9 and 11 and then choose 12, 13, 14, 15, 16, or 17. If you used one of these numbers, you would put it in the data set so the numbers are still arranged from least to greatest.) Here, the value 10 has been chosen to complete the data set:

9 , 10 , 11 , 11 , 18

LEARN

ANSWER A data set that has five data points, a range of 9, and one mode is 9, 10, 11, 11, 18.

LOOK BACK Review the data set you created and compare it to the information in the problem to check that the data set meets all the requirements.

Use the information given to create a data set.

1. Create a data set that has two modes and a median of 12.

2. Create a data set that has five data points, no modes, and a mean of 6.

3. Create a data set that has six data points and a median of 6.5.

4. Create a data set that has six data points and three modes.

5. Create a data set with five data points, one mode, a median of 5, and a mean of 7.

6. Create a data set with seven data points, a range of 50, two modes, a median of 48, and a mean of 45.

LEARN

Organize Data to Draw Histograms (A)

Organize Data in a Frequency Table

Worked Examples

You can record data in a frequency table as one way to organize and display data.

PROBLEM In a survey, people were asked how old they had been when they learned to ride a bike. Their replies are in this table. Create a frequency table with this data.

Age When Learned to Ride a Bike			
28	13	11	9
20	13	11	9
18	13	10	8
16	13	10	8
15	12	10	8
13	12	9	7
13	12	9	7

SOLUTION

1 To make a frequency table, draw a table with 3 columns. Put a title at the top. Label the columns.

- The first column is for naming ranges. This column heading will be "Age range."
- The middle column, "Tally," is for writing tally marks to record the data.
- The third column, "Frequency," is for recording the frequency of the data.

2 Decide on the age ranges for rows in the first column. You can have age ranges of 7–10, 11–13, and 15–28. You can have more age ranges if you want to have more rows.

3 Start at the top left-hand side of the data table. Make a tally mark in the middle column of the frequency table for each age data point. Put the tally mark in the correct "Age range" row.

4 After you have finished, count the tally marks in each row. That number is the frequency. Write the frequency for each row in the third column.

ANSWER

Age When Learned to Ride a Bike		
Age range	Tally	Frequency
7–10	卌 卌 ||	12
11–13	卌 卌		11
15–28	卌	5

L E A R N

Follow the directions to complete the activity.

1. Create a frequency table for the data. Write a title and column headings. Then put the frequency data in the table. Group the heights so you have one column with ranges of numbers in a logical sequence, such as 60–79, 80–99, 100–119, and so on. In the second column, use tally marks to record the number of heights within the ranges. In the third column, write the frequency number.

Tall Ferris Wheels			
Ferris wheel	**Height (meters)**	**Ferris wheel**	**Height (meters)**
Beijing Great Wheel	208	Harbin Ferris Wheel	110
Great Berlin Wheel	175	Jinjiang Park Ferris Wheel	108
Singapore Flyer	165	HEP Five	106
Star of Nanchang	160	Grande Roue de Paris	100
London Eye	135	Space Eye	100
Suzhou Ferris Wheel	120	The Great Wheel	94
The Southern Star	120	Aurora Wheel	90
Tianjin Eye	120	Eurowheel	90
Changsha Ferris Wheel	120	Janfusun Fancyworld	88
Zhengzhou Ferris Wheel	120	Mashhad Fun Fair	80
Sky Dream Fukuoka	120	The Ferris Wheel (original Ferris wheel)	80
Diamond and Flowers Ferris Wheel	117	Moscow-850	75
Sky Wheel of Odaiba	115	Polaris Tower	72
Star of Tai Lake	115	Miramar Ferris Wheel	70
Cosmo Clock 21	112.5	Texas Star	65
Tempozan Harbor Village Ferris Wheel	112.5	Riesenrad Vienna	64.8

LEARN

Organize Data to Draw Histograms (A)

Work with Frequency Tables

Follow the directions to complete the activity.

1. Create a frequency table for the data.

   - Write a title and column headings.
   - Put the frequency data in the table. Group the number of books people read so the first column has ranges of numbers in a logical sequence. Use 5-book ranges starting with 1–5, 6–10, and so on.
   - In the second column, use tally marks to record the number of people within the ranges.
   - In the third column, write the frequency number.

Book Club	
Name	Number of books read in September, October, and November
Betty	12
David	4
Sonia	2
Sophia	15
Steven	7
Paul	9
Bob	20
Marcia	21
Mary	16
Rob	3
Eric	14
Mark	9
Brian	14
Carl	20
Jared	6

T R Y I T

Choose the answer.

2. Maurice recorded the number of minutes he did yard work each week for 6 weeks. Which frequency table shows the data?

Week 1: 45 minutes
Week 2: 65 minutes
Week 3: 110 minutes
Week 4: 75 minutes
Week 5: 60 minutes
Week 6: 30 minutes

A.

Yard Work		
Time (minutes)	Tally	Frequency
0–19	|	1
20–39		0
40–59	||	2
60–79	||	2
80–99		0
100–119	|	1

B.

Yard Work		
Time (minutes)	Tally	Frequency
0–19	|	1
20–39	|	1
40–59	|||	3
60–79	|	1
80–99		0
100–119		0

C.

Yard Work		
Time (minutes)	Tally	Frequency
0–19		0
20–39	|	1
40–59	|	1
60–79	|||	3
80–99		0
100–119	|	1

TRY IT

3. Lara recorded the number of hours she exercised each month for a year. Which frequency table shows the data?

January: 8 hours
February: 7 hours
March: 10 hours
April: 8 hours
May: 14 hours
June: 20 hours
July: 22 hours
August: 8 hours
September: 10 hours
October: 9 hours
November: 11 hours
December: 6 hours

A.

Exercise		
Time (hours)	Tally	Frequency
0–4		0
5–9	|||||	5
10–14	|||||	5
15–19			1
20–24			1

B.

Exercise		
Time (hours)	Tally	Frequency
0–4		0
5–9	||||||	6
10–14	||||	4
15–19		0
20–24	||	2

C.

Exercise		
Time (hours)	Tally	Frequency
0–4	||||||	6
5–9		0
10–14	|||	3
15–19		0
20–24	|||	3

TRY IT

4. Deborah recorded the number of servings of fruit that each member of her ballet class ate in one week. Which frequency table shows the data?

Helen: 15

Jane: 9

Gillian: 13

Danielle: 19

Nina: 8

Sally: 17

Vanessa: 18

Claire: 13

Zoe: 12

A.

Fruit Eaten in One Week

Number	Tally	Frequency
0–5		0
6–10	||	2
11–15	||||	4
16–20	|||	3
21–25		0

B.

Fruit Eaten in One Week

Number	Tally	Frequency
0–5		0
6–10	|||	3
11–15	|||	3
16–20	|||	3
21–25	|||	3

C.

Fruit Eaten in One Week

Number	Tally	Frequency
0–5	|	1
6–10	||	2
11–15	||||	4
16–20	|||	3
21–25		0

Organize Data to Draw Histograms (B)

Make a Histogram

Worked Examples

A histogram is a graph that displays the data from a frequency table. Histograms have bars that represent data. The bars are usually all the same width. The width depends on the range of measurements in the frequency table. The heights of the bars depend on the frequency data.

A histogram has a horizontal axis (the bottom line of the graph) and a vertical axis (the line along the left side of the graph). Each axis is labeled with a name and with numbers that are used for placement of the bars.

World's Longest Roller Coasters		
Length range (feet)	Tally	Frequency
2,000–4,000	|||	3
4,001–6,000	||||	4
6,001–8,000	||||		6
8,001–10,000	|||| ||	7
10,001–12,000	||	2

PROBLEM Draw a histogram to display the data in the frequency table.

SOLUTION

1 Write a title at the top of the histogram. The title should describe the data in the frequency table, such as "World's Longest Roller Coasters."

2 Label the horizontal axis and the vertical axis. For the horizontal axis label, write the column name for the range of measurements in the frequency table: "Length range (feet)." For the vertical axis label, write "Frequency."

3 Mark off 5 even sections along the horizontal axis for ranges and write the ranges from the frequency table below the axis. As you mark off the ranges, don't put space between them. The bars on a histogram sit right next to each other.

4 Number the vertical axis. Histograms often show one number greater than the greatest number in the frequency table. When the vertical axis includes one greater number, the scale is easier to read. The frequency table has frequencies from 0 to 7, so number the vertical axis from 0 to 8.

5 Draw a bar for the first range, 2,000–4,000. The frequency is 3, so the bar should stop at the 3 along on the vertical axis. Using the data in the frequency table, draw and shade a bar for each range (each row in the frequency table should have one bar in the histogram). Use a ruler to draw the bars.

L E A R N

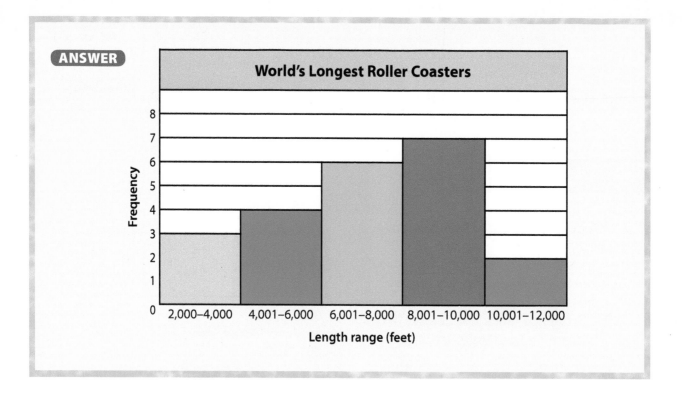

World's Longest Roller Coasters

Frequency

8
7
6
5
4
3
2
1
0

2,000–4,000   4,001–6,000   6,001–8,000   8,001–10,000   10,001–12,000

Length range (feet)

Follow the steps to draw a histogram to display the data in the frequency table.

1. Write a title at the top of the histogram.

2. Label the horizontal axis.

3. Number the vertical axis.

4. Write the ranges on the horizontal axis.

5. Draw and shade a bar for each range in the frequency table

Tall Ferris Wheels		
Height range (meters)	Tally	Frequency
60–79	╫╫	5
80–99	╫╫ |	6
100–119	╫╫ ╫╫	10
120–139	╫╫ ||	7
140–159		0
160–179	|||	3
180–199		0
200–219	|	1

Organize Data to Draw Histograms (B)

Make a Frequency Table and Histogram

Worked Examples

You can use the data in a table to create a frequency table and a histogram.

PROBLEM This table shows the coldest water temperatures at a lake for two weeks in December. Create a frequency table and a histogram to represent the data.

SOLUTION

1 For the frequency table, divide the data into ranges. Logical ranges would be 38.0–40.9, 41.0–43.9, and 44.0–46.9. Make the columns. Write the tally marks and the frequency numbers in the correct columns.

2 Use the frequency table to draw a histogram. On the horizontal axis, write the ranges from the frequency table. Number the vertical axis to show all the frequencies. Draw bars to represent the data.

Lake Temperatures		
Day	Temperature in week 1 (°F)	Temperature in week 2 (°F)
Sunday	44.0	38.7
Monday	41.5	38.2
Tuesday	39.2	40.0
Wednesday	39.5	42.1
Thursday	40.3	42.5
Friday	38.0	44.8
Saturday	39.6	45.1

ANSWER

Frequency Table

Lake Temperatures		
Temperature range (°F)	Tally	Frequency
38.0– 40.9	卌 |||	8
41.0– 43.9	|||	3
44.0– 46.9	|||	3

Histogram

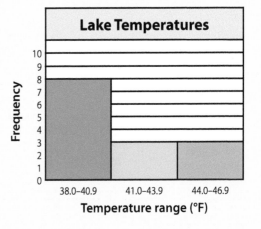

L E A R N

Use the table to answer Problems 1–9.

Frogtown is located in California between Yosemite National Park and Lake Tahoe, south of Historic Angels Camp. The table shows the Frog Jump Results data.

Frog Jump Results		
Frog's name	Frog jockey	Distance
Lisa Can Do	Brent	21 ft 4 in.
Jumpin' Daly	Joseph	20 ft 5 in.
To Be or Not to Be	Gavin	19 ft 10 in.
Kasha	Jacob	19 ft 6 in.
Don't You Wish	Bob	19 ft
Buck Shot	Michael	18 ft 9 in.
Worthless Chris	Craig	18 ft 6 in.
Papi	Kevin	18 ft 5 in.

Follow the steps to draw a frequency table to represent the data.

1. Give the frequency table a title. Label the columns.

2. Decide what the ranges will be. Write the ranges in the first column in ascending order.

3. Tally the data for each range. Write the tally marks in the middle column.

4. Count the tally marks for each row. Write the number for each row in the "Frequency" column.

Follow the steps to draw a histogram to display the data in the frequency table.

5. Write a title at the top of the histogram.

6. Label the horizontal axis.

7. Number the vertical axis.

8. Write the ranges on the horizontal axis.

9. Draw and shade a bar for each range in the frequency table.

LEARN

Organize Data to Draw Histograms (B)

Make and Interpret Histograms

Use the table to answer Problems 1–5. Follow the steps to draw a histogram to display the data in the frequency table.

Visitors to National Parks		
Numbers of visitors	Tally	Frequency
0–99,999	卌 |||	8
100,000–199,999	|||	3
200,000 –299,999	||	2
300,000–399,999	|||	3

1. Write a title at the top of the histogram.

2. Label the horizontal axis.

3. Number the vertical axis.

4. Write the ranges on the horizontal axis.

5. Draw and shade a bar for each range in the frequency table.

TRY IT

Choose the answer.

6. Nadia recorded the number of letters each person in her summer camp group sent home each week. She then organized the information in a frequency table.

Number of Letters Sent		
Number of letters	Tally	Frequency
0–2	卌 卌	10
3–5	卌	5
6–8	|||	3

Which histogram correctly displays this information?

A.

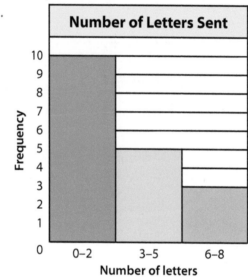

B.

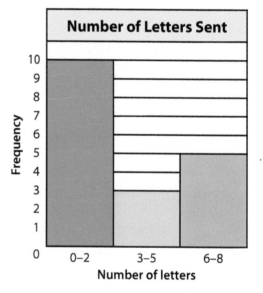

C.

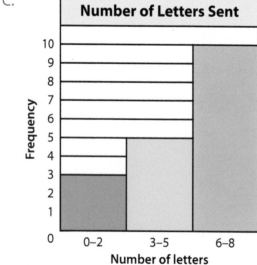

TRY IT

7. Dave recorded the number of runs he scored in each baseball game in one season. He then organized the information in a frequency table.

Runs Scored		
Runs	Tally	Frequency
0–3	|||	3
4–7	||	2
8–11			1

Which histogram correctly displays this information?

A.

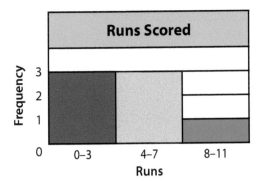

B.

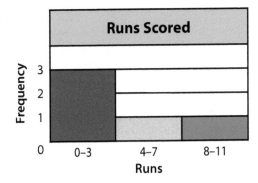

C.

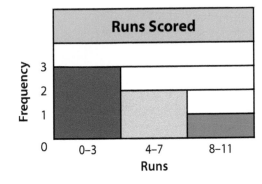

8. Bobbi recorded the number of points she scored in each basketball game she played during the summer. She then organized the information in a frequency table.

Points Scored		
Points	Tally	Frequency
0–9	|||	3
10–19	||||	4
20–29	||	2
30–39	~~||||~~	5
40–49	||	2

Which histogram correctly displays this information?

A.

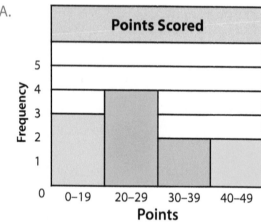

B.

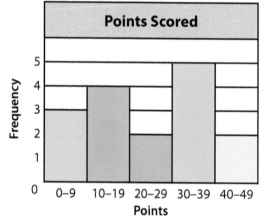

C.

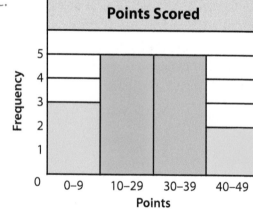

TRY IT

Create Circle Graphs

Organize Data on a Circle Graph

Worked Examples

You can use data to create a circle graph.

PROBLEM Students answered a survey on their favorite type of book: adventure, science fiction, or mystery. The students' responses were adventure, 25; science fiction, 20; and mystery, 5. Show the data in a circle graph.

SOLUTION

1 Find the sum of the data values: $25 + 20 + 5 = 50$. There were 50 students who took part in the survey.

2 Find a fraction to represent each data value. The denominator of each fraction will be 50 because 50 students took part in the survey. Then change each fraction to a percent.

- To represent 25 students, write $\frac{25}{50}$. Change it to a percent. $\frac{25}{50} = \frac{50}{100} = 50\%$

- To represent 20 students, write $\frac{20}{50}$. Change it to a percent. $\frac{20}{50} = \frac{40}{100} = 40\%$

- To represent 5 students, write $\frac{5}{50}$. Change it to a percent. $\frac{5}{50} = \frac{10}{100} = 10\%$

3 Add to make sure the sum of the percents is 100%. $50 + 40 + 10 = 100$

4 Using your ruler, divide your circle into 50%, 40%, and 10% sections. It's acceptable to draw only approximate sizes for the sections. Always label your sections so that it's clear what portion of the circle they represent.

- Start by drawing a line through the circle to divide it in half. Label one of the halves "Adventure 50%."

- Then divide the other half into two sections, for 10% and 40%. The 40% section should look like it's about 4 times as large as the 10% section. Label the sections "Science fiction 40%" and "Mystery 10%."

5 Write a title above the circle graph that accurately describes the data.

LEARN

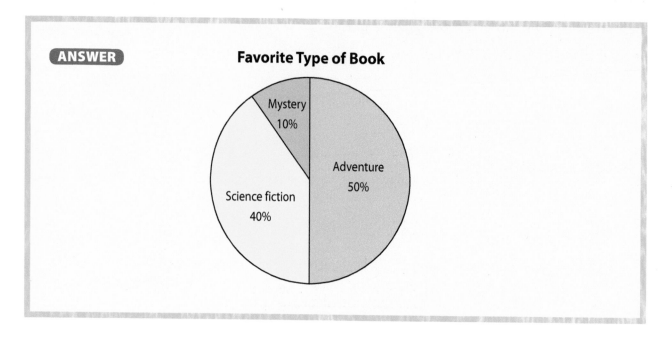

Favorite Type of Book

Mystery 10%

Science fiction 40%

Adventure 50%

Use the data in the table to create a circle graph.

Students were surveyed about their favorite activities.

Favorite Activities	
Activity	Number of students
Watching movies	20
Playing with pets	80
Reading	10
Playing team sports	40
Playing outdoors	10

1. Find the sum of the students surveyed.

2. Find a fraction to represent each value.

3. Divide the circle into fractional sections for the data points.

4. Write the description of the data and the value in each appropriate section of the circle graph.

5. Write a title above the circle graph.

Use the data in the table to create a circle graph.

Kendall created a table to show how he spends his monthly allowance.

Monthly Allowance	
What money was used for	Amount
Savings	$72
Movies	$12
Snacks	$6
Charity	$6

6. Find the sum of the money amounts in Kendall's table.

7. Find a fraction to represent each value.

8. Divide the circle into fractional sections for the data points.

9. Write the description of the data and the value in each appropriate section of the circle graph.

10. Write a title above the circle graph.

Make a table and create a circle graph to represent the data.

11. Nicole asked 36 friends what their favorite type of movie is. Nine said they liked comedies best. Eighteen said adventure movies were their favorite. The rest liked nature movies best.

CREATE CIRCLE GRAPHS

LEARN